GLENCOE

PHYSICS

Principles and Problems

Chapter Assessment

McGraw-Hill

New York, New York Columbus, Ohio Woodland Hills, California Peoria, Illinois

GLENCOE

PHYSICS

Principles and Problems

Student Edition

Teacher Wraparound Edition

Teacher Classroom Resources

- Transparency Package with Transparency Masters
- Laboratory Manual SE and TE
- Physics Lab and Pocket Lab Worksheets
- Study Guide SE and TE
- Chapter Assessment
- Tech Prep Applications
- Critical Thinking
- Reteaching
- Enrichment
- Physics Skills
- Advanced Concepts in Physics
- Supplemental Problems
- Problems and Solutions Manual
- Spanish Resources
- Lesson Plans with block scheduling

Technology

- Computer Test Bank (Win/Mac)
- MindJogger Videoquizzes
- Electronic Teacher Classroom Resources (ETCR)
- Website at *www.glencoe.com/sec/science*
- Physics for the Computer Age CD-ROM (Win/Mac)

The Glencoe Science Professional Development Series

- Graphing Calculators in the Science Classroom
- Cooperative Learning in the Science Classroom
- Alternate Assessment in the Science Classroom
- Performance Assessment in the Science Classroom
- Lab and Safety Skills in the Science Classroom

Glencoe/McGraw-Hill

A Division of The ***McGraw-Hill*** *Companies*

Send all inquiries to:
Glencoe/McGraw-Hill
8787 Orion Place
Columbus, Ohio 43240

ISBN 0-02-825492-9
Printed in the United States of America.

3 4 5 6 7 8 9 045 05 04 03 02 01 00

Contents

To the Teacher

This *Chapter Assessment* booklet provides materials to assess your students' success in ***Physics: Principles and Problems.*** Each chapter test includes three sections that assess understanding of concepts both qualitatively and quantitatively.

- Understanding Concepts Part A consists of a variety of objective formats such as matching, multiple choice, and true/false. The items in this section assess students' understanding of vocabulary and basic facts presented in the chapter.
- Understanding Concepts Part B consists of problems. Generally, these problems require minimal steps to solve.
- Applying Concepts consists of items that assess students' ability to extend their learning to new situations. Again, assessment is done first qualitatively—through short-answer questions—and then quantitatively—through problems. The problems in this section are more difficult than those presented earlier and generally require more calculations as well as a deeper comprehension of the chapter concepts.

Comprehension of concepts can also be assessed through performance—by carrying out a process and providing a product. You can use the information on the following pages to help you incorporate performance assessment into your classroom.

Performance Assessment

Performance assessment gives you a more complete evaluation of your students' progress. By carrying out a process, students are presented with a wide range of choices with which to demonstrate their learning. Opportunities for performance assessment are plentiful in a physics classroom. For example, a physics experiment requires students to engage their knowledge, skills, and learning habits to carry out a process and provide a product. That product may include a table of data, a graph, a calculated value, a conclusion, a model, a description, or other possibilities. Experiments provide concrete outcomes for your evaluation and give students the opportunity to demonstrate proficiency in skill areas that go beyond content recall. Extensions and applications at the end of experiments provide further such opportunities.

Evaluation Forms

Two evaluation forms are provided for you to photocopy and use as tools to assess student performance. You might want to use one or both, or you might use parts of them to design your own form.

Individual Evaluation Form This form can be used to record observations about the performance of an individual student. It contains a scoring key and lists progress indicators and skills that can apply to a wide variety of assessment tasks.

Classroom Evaluation Form You might want to use this form to make notes on various students' efforts during assessment tasks. The form lists ten processes that students should be expected to demonstrate. If you are using the classroom form only, you might want to add some of the indicators from the individual evaluation form by simply writing them in.

Evaluation Key Rubric

The evaluation forms give you indicators to help you spot areas of progress, and the evaluation key provides a system for scoring work. However, the scoring of performance assessment relies on your own knowledge of your students as much as it does on specific criteria.

It is suggested that you assign values to students' work according to the following general rubric.

4 Highest performance	The student at this level demonstrates thorough capability and provides new insight.
3 Proficiency	The student at this level demonstrates complete capability.
2 Acceptable performance	The student at this level demonstrates partial capability.
1 Low or incomplete performance	The student at this level either has not done the work or has challenges to overcome before demonstrating any capability.

Performance Assessment
Individual Evaluation Form

Student:

Date:

Chapter:

Task:

Evaluation Key

4 Highest performance

3 Proficiency

2 Acceptable performance

1 Low or incomplete performance

Indicator	Process	Evaluation			
Acquiring knowledge					
Notices details and finds evidence	Observing	1	2	3	4
Sorts new information effectively	Classifying	1	2	3	4
Forms effective questions	Hypothesizing	1	2	3	4
Gathers sufficient information	Observing	1	2	3	4
Extending knowledge					
Makes an accurate record	Communicating	1	2	3	4
Constructs a graph	Interpreting data	1	2	3	4
Constructs a useful model	Using models	1	2	3	4
Uses an experiment effectively	Using variables	1	2	3	4
Using knowledge meaningfully					
Chooses appropriate examples	Critical thinking	1	2	3	4
Completes a report, exhibit, performance, or other form of presentation	Communicating	1	2	3	4
Applies results to consumer decisions and behavior	Critical thinking	1	2	3	4
Forms an argument	Communicating	1	2	3	4
Habits and attitudes					
Works well within a group	Cooperating	1	2	3	4
Respects other points of view	Critical thinking	1	2	3	4
Continues working when frustrated	Self-managing	1	2	3	4
Responds to feedback; evaluates own work	Self-managing	1	2	3	4

Comments:

Performance Assessment
Classroom Evaluation Form

Date:

Chapter:

Task:

Evaluation Key

4 Highest performance

3 Proficiency

2 Acceptable performance

1 Low or incomplete performance

Student	Observing	Classifying	Hypothesizing	Communicating	Interpreting data	Using models	Using variables	Critical thinking	Cooperating	Self-managing

Date ______________ Period ______________ Name ______________________________

1 Chapter Assessment

Use with Chapter 1.

What is physics?

Understanding Concepts

Write the letter of the choice that best completes each statement.

_____ **1.** Physics is the study of _____.

- **a.** matter and cells
- **b.** energy and heat
- **c.** energy and atoms
- **d.** matter and energy

_____ **2.** Ancient Greek scholars believed that all matter on or near Earth was made of _____ elements.

- **a.** 1
- **b.** 4
- **c.** 100
- **d.** 111

_____ **3.** Ancient Greek scholars believed that celestial objects were formed from _____.

- **a.** air
- **b.** fire
- **c.** light
- **d.** quintessence

_____ **4.** _____ is considered to be the father of modern experimental science.

- **a.** Albert Einstein
- **b.** Aristotle
- **c.** Galileo Galilei
- **d.** Louis Pasteur

_____ **5.** The first successful landing and operation of a vehicle on the surface of Mars took place during the _____ mission.

- **a.** *Global Surveyor*
- **b.** *Mariner 9*
- **c.** *Phobos 2*
- **d.** *Viking 1*

Name ______________________

1 Chapter Assessment

For each of the statements below, write true *or rewrite the italicized part to make the statement true.*

6. Planets were called wanderers by ancient people because their *brightness* differed from the stars.

____

7. Greek philosophers thought that *motion* occurred because an element traveled in a straight line to its own natural place.

____

8. Galileo was the first to discover that the moon had *an atmosphere.*

____

9. Galileo argued that the planets circled *Earth.*

____

10. In the scientific method, conclusions are tested to find out whether they are *valid.*

____

Applying Concepts

Answer the following questions, using complete sentences.

1. Describe how physicists study problems in an organized way.

____

____

____

2. What are the three functions of a scientific explanation?

____

____

____

3. What is similar in the ways scientists study problems?

____

____

____

____

4. What information might scientists learn from studying the Martian atmosphere?

____

____

____

Name ______________________

1 Chapter Assessment

5. What are some benefits of working on a team?

6. Describe two applications that resulted from the work of physicists.

Date ______________ Period ______________ Name ______________________

2 Chapter Assessment

Use with Chapter 2.

A Mathematical Toolkit

Understanding Concepts Part A

Write the letter of the choice that best completes each statement.

_____ **1.** The base SI unit for time is the _____.

a. minute
b. day
c. second
d. hour

_____ **2.** In scientific notation, a number between 1 and 10 is multiplied by _____.

a. a whole-number power of 10
b. a fraction
c. 10
d. any whole number

_____ **3.** The metric prefix that means 1/1 000 000 000 is _____.

a. pico
b. nano
c. centi
d. giga

_____ **4.** To avoid parallax errors, laboratory instruments should be read _____.

a. at eye level
b. from the side
c. below eye level
d. at all of these positions

_____ **5.** The slope of a straight-line graph is the rise _____ the run.

a. added to
b. subtracted from
c. multiplied by
d. divided by

For each of the statements below, write true *or rewrite the italicized part to make the statement true.*

6. ______________________ The unit of speed, m/s, is an example of a *base* unit.

7. ______________________ The degree of exactness to which the measurement of a quantity can be reproduced is called *accuracy*.

8. ______________________ A variable that can be manipulated in an experiment is the *independent* variable.

9. ______________________ When constructing a graph from data, the range of the *x*-axis is determined by the range of the *dependent* variable.

10. ______________________ A graph that is a hyperbola represents an *inverse* relationship.

11. ______________________ A graph that is a parabola represents a *linear* relationship.

Name ______________________

2 Chapter Assessment

Understanding Concepts Part B

Answer the following questions.

1. Express the measurements in scientific notation.

a. 142 000 s ______________________

b. 0.008 09 kg ______________________

c. 501 000 000 m ______________________

2. Simplify the expressions. Give your answers in scientific notation, using the correct number of significant digits.

a. $(2 \times 10^6 \text{ m})(5 \times 10^5 \text{ m})$ ______________________

b. $(12 \times 10^6 \text{ m})/(4 \times 10^2 \text{ s})$ ______________________

c. $(5.06 \times 10^2 \text{ m}) + (8.124 \text{ km})$ ______________________

3. Describe the relationship between the variables shown in the graph below. Identify the general equation that is used to represent this type of relationship.

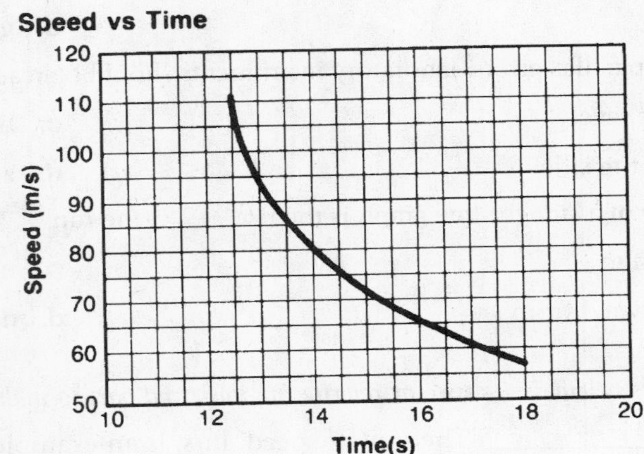

____

____

____

4. Identify the slope and *y*-intercept of the equation

Fahrenheit Temperature = (1.8°F/°C)(*Celsius Temperature*) + 32°F.

____

Name ______________________

2 Chapter Assessment

Applying Concepts

Answer the following questions, using complete sentences.

1. Describe the relationship between base units and derived units.

____

____

2. Which of the following is a more precise measurement, the length of a tabletop measured with a stick calibrated in centimeters as shown on the left, or the length measured with a stick calibrated in millimeters as shown on the right? Give a reason for your answer.

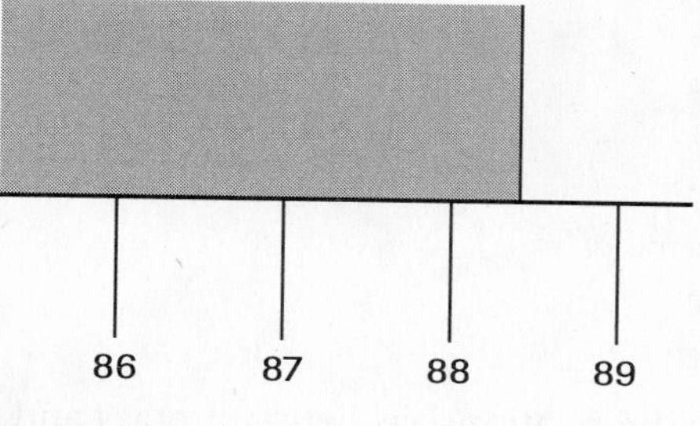

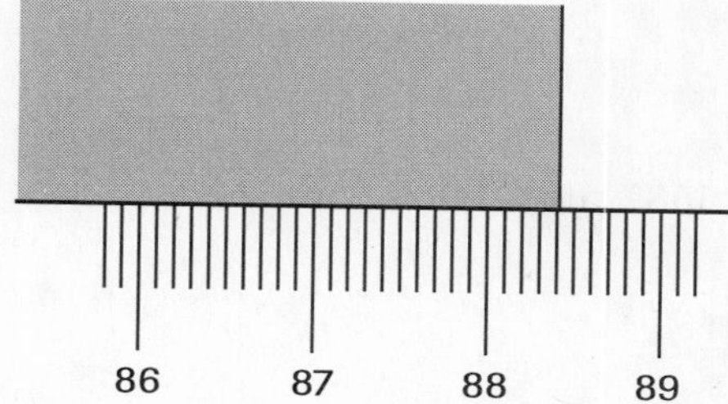

____

____

3. Express the measurements in the diagram above in centimeters. ______________________

4. Explain the difference between accuracy and precision.

____

____

5. Give the number of significant digits in each measurement.

a. 3809 m ________ **b.** 9.013 m ________ **c.** 0.0045 m ________

6. Which of the following measurements contains zeros that are *not* significant? Give a reason for your answer.

3.050×10^5 mm   0.0053 m   45.020 cm   101.20 g

____

____

____

7. How are independent and dependent variables related? Identify the graph axis on which each type of variable would be plotted.

____

____

Name ______________________

2 Chapter Assessment

Answer the following questions, showing your calculations.

8. The total mass of four containers is 5.000 kg. If the mass of container A is 256 mg, container B is 5117 cg, and container C is 382 g, what is the mass of container D?

9. Show that the measurements in each pair are equivalent.

a. 0.002 35 Ts, 2350 Ms

b. 5687 nm , 0.000 056 87 dm

10. The results of a class experiment investigating the relationship between mass and acceleration are shown in the table below. The force applied to each mass remained constant.

Mass (kg)	Acceleration (m/s^2)
0.5	6.0
1.0	3.0
1.5	2.0
2.0	1.5
2.5	1.2
3.0	1.0

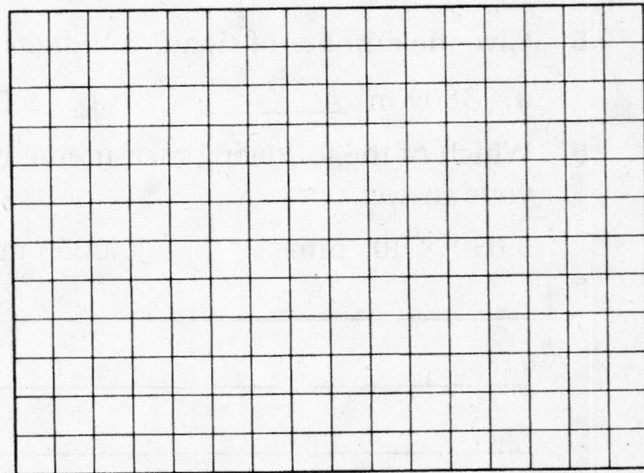

a. Plot the values given and draw the curve that best fits the points.

b. Describe the resulting curve.

____

c. What is the relationship between mass and the acceleration produced by a constant force?

____

____

d. What is the general equation for the relationship shown in the graph?

____

____

Date ______________ Period ______________ Name ______________________

3 Chapter Assessment

Use with Chapter 3.

Describing Motion

Understanding Concepts Part A

For each of the statements below, write true *or rewrite the italicized part to make the statement true.*

1. ______________________ A series of images of an object that records its position after equal time intervals is called a motion diagram.

2. ______________________ No change in the position of an object in successive frames of a motion diagram is an operational definition of an object *with a positive acceleration*.

3. ______________________ A particle model can be used to represent a moving object if the size of the object is *much greater than* the distance it moves.

4. ______________________ To study the motion of a sprinter, the *finish line* would be one choice for the origin of a coordinate system.

5. ______________________ Each of the four motion diagrams below shows the position of an object at successive 1-s time intervals. *Diagram A* shows an object with a constant positive acceleration.

A Begin • • • • • • • • • End

B Begin • • • • • • • • • • End

C Begin • • • • • End

D Begin • • • • • • • • End

6. ______________________ Of the four diagrams above, the object in *diagram A* had the largest average velocity for any time interval.

7. ______________________ Displacement is to distance as velocity is to *acceleration*.

8. ______________________ The *displacement* of an object is equal to the product of its average velocity and the time interval.

9. ______________________ The ratio of the change in average velocity to the time interval in which the change is made is defined as *average acceleration*.

10. ______________________ If a truck has a negative velocity and a negative acceleration, the truck is *slowing down* in the negative direction.

Name ______________________

3 Chapter Assessment

Understanding Concepts Part B

Create pictorial and physical models for each of the following problems. Do not solve the problem.

1. A hockey puck's average velocity is 22 m/s. What is its displacement in 6.0 s?

2. A car maintains an acceleration of 0.6 m/s^2 from rest for 5.0 s. How far does it move in this time?

Name ______________________

3 Chapter Assessment

Applying Concepts

Answer the following questions, using complete sentences.

1. When looking at an object recorded in successive frames by a camcorder, how can you determine if the object is moving?

2. How can you operationally define the constant speed of an object, using successive frames of a camcorder?

3. How can an object have a *negative* position?

4. From observing successive camcorder frames in which two objects are moving, how can you determine which of the two objects is moving faster?

5. Explain how a moving object could have a motion diagram that is the same as that of an object at rest.

6. My house is 5 minutes away from school by bike. How am I operationally defining distance?

7. Explain what is meant by an object having an acceleration of $+8\ m/s^2$.

Name ______________________________

3 Chapter Assessment

Set up the pictorial and physical models for each of the following problems. You need not solve the problem.

8. A tennis ball is released at the top of a 2-m ramp and rolls down with an acceleration of 1.0 m/s^2. The ball reaches the end of the ramp in 2.0 s and rolls onto the floor. If the ball experiences an average acceleration of -0.5 m/s^2 as it rolls along the floor, how far from the end of the ramp will the ball stop?

9. While jogging, Maria sees Jason 15 m ahead of her, walking in the same direction. If Maria is jogging at 5.0 m/s and Jason is walking at 2.0 m/s, how far will Maria have to jog before catching up to Jason?

Date ______________ Period ______________ Name ______________________

4 Chapter Assessment

Use with Chapter 4.

Vector Addition

Understanding Concepts Part A

Write the letter of the choice that best completes the statement or answers the question.

______ **1.** The downstream velocity of a river that flows south _____ a boat's eastward velocity.

a. slightly increases

b. slightly decreases

c. has no effect on

______ **2.** When adding vectors graphically, the direction and length of each vector must _____.

a. be similar to the direction and length of the resultant.

b. not be changed

c. be reversed

______ **3.** You walked 10 km west and then ran 10 km north. During each part of the journey, the _____ was the same.

a. distance

b. displacement

c. speed

d. velocity

______ **4.** The magnitude of the resultant vector is _____.

a. the difference between the magnitudes of the original vectors

b. the sum of the magnitudes of the original vectors

c. calculated using the Law of Cosines

______ **5.** A runner is 5.0 km east of another runner, who is 5.0 km east of a parking lot. Where is the first runner with respect to the parking lot?

a. 5 km east of the lot

b. 10 km east of the lot

c. at the lot

d. −5 km east of the lot

For each situation below, write the letter of the matching item.

______ **6.** A hiker walks 15 km due east, then heads due north for 8 km. What is the direction of the resultant vector?

______ **7.** After a bike ride, your displacement is 10 km, 30° east of north. In which direction is your displacement greatest?

______ **8.** A swimmer wants to swim due east in a stream that flows due south. In which direction should the swimmer swim?

______ **9.** The vertical and horizontal components of a vector are both negative values in a coordinate system. If the vector is in quadrant III, in what direction does the *x*-axis point?

a. east

b. north

c. northeast

d. south

e. southeast

f. west

Name ______________________

4 Chapter Assessment

Understanding Concepts Part B

Answer the following questions, showing your calculations.

1. You exercised by walking for 15 minutes on a treadmill that has a level track that moves at a velocity of −4 km/h.

a. What was your velocity relative to the treadmill track while you were exercising?

____

b. What was your velocity relative to the floor while you were exercising?

____

c. What was your total displacement relative to the treadmill track when you finished exercising?

____

d. What was your total displacement relative to the floor when you finished exercising?

____

2. A rubber ball strikes a wall at a velocity of 30 km/h and rebounds with a velocity of –20 km/h. What is the change of velocity of the ball?

3. A hot-air balloon is ascending straight upward at 30 km/h in air that is blowing horizontally at 8 km/h. What is the horizontal velocity of the balloon relative to the wind?

____

4. Find the components of the velocity of a car that is moving at 30.0 km/h in a direction 35.0° north of east.

5. A runner jogs 8.0 km west, turns and jogs 10.0 km south, and then jogs 7.0 km north at a constant speed. Graphically determine the magnitude and direction of the jogger's displacement.

Name ______________________

4 Chapter Assessment

Applying Concepts

Answer these questions, showing your calculations.

1. Describe how to add two perpendicular velocity vectors.

____

____

____

____

2. Describe how to add two vectors, using their components.

____

____

____

____

____

3. A problem involves a box placed on an incline. A coordinate system is chosen so that the *x*-axis is parallel to the incline and the positive direction points up the incline.

a. Describe the motion of the box if it has a negative velocity in this coordinate system.

____

b. Describe the motion of the box if it has a positive velocity at 90.0° in this coordinate system.

____

4. The diagram below shows two vectors representing the route a person took from home. Draw the vector that indicates the most direct route home.

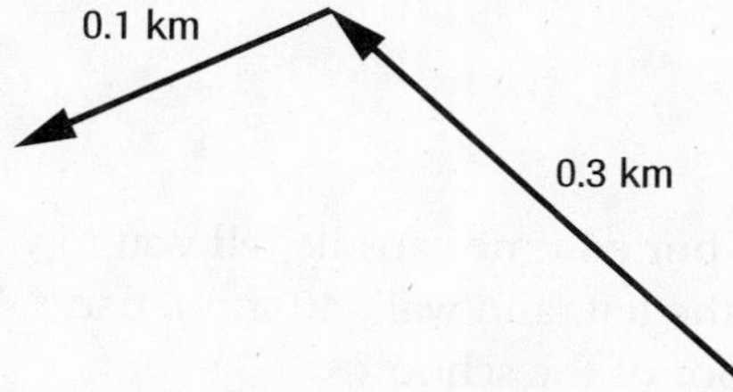

5. Two displacement vectors have equal magnitudes of 8 km. Describe the two vectors if their sum has the following values: 0 km, 8 km, and 16 km.

____

____

____

Name ______________________

4 Chapter Assessment

6. Determine trigonometrically the magnitude and direction of the velocity of a plane that is flying west at 100.0 km/h with respect to the air while the wind is blowing toward the north at 65.0 km/h relative to the ground.

7. A pilot wants to fly a plane at 500.0 km/h, directly north. The wind is blowing at 90.0 km/h from the east. Find the magnitude and direction of the course the pilot should fly.

8. A soccer ball is rolling east at an average velocity of 6.0 m/s when a kick deflects it to the north at an average velocity of 7.0 m/s. What is the magnitude and direction of the ball's change of velocity?

9. The directions to locate a buried time capsule tell you to walk 50 paces west from the front door of your school, turn 80° to the left, and walk 40 more paces. What is the magnitude of the capsule's displacement from the door of the school?

Date ______________ Period ______________ Name ______________________

5 Chapter Assessment

Use with Chapter 5.

A Mathematical Model of Motion

Understanding Concepts Part A

For each description on the left, write the letter of the matching item.

_____ **1.** the slope of the tangent to a curve of a position-time graph

_____ **2.** change of position of an object

_____ **3.** displacement divided by the time interval during which the displacement took place

_____ **4.** motion in which equal displacements take place in successive equal time periods

_____ **5.** change of velocity divided by the time interval during which the change took place

_____ **6.** the slope of the tangent to a curve of a velocity-time graph

_____ **7.** motion that is described by a line of constant slope on a velocity-time graph

_____ **8.** the constant acceleration that acts on falling bodies

a. constant acceleration
b. instantaneous velocity
c. uniform motion
d. average acceleration
e. displacement
f. instantaneous acceleration
g. acceleration due to gravity
h. average velocity

For each of the statements below, write true *or rewrite the italicized part to make the statement true.*

9. On a position-time graph, the average velocity equals the *run multiplied* by the rise.

____

10. A child drops a ball. The instantaneous velocity of the ball as the child lets go is *zero*.

____

11. A child drops a ball. The instantaneous acceleration of the ball as the child lets go is *zero*.

____

12 A toy rocket is launched vertically upward. When the rocket reaches its highest point, its velocity is *at its maximum*.

____

Name ______________________

5 Chapter Assessment

Understanding Concepts Part B

1. A skateboard rider starts from rest and maintains a constant acceleration of $+0.50\ m/s^2$ for 8.4 s. What is the rider's displacement during this time?

2. A sports car can move 100.0 m in the first 4.5 s of uniform acceleration. Find the car's acceleration.

3. A rolling ball has an initial velocity of -1.6 m/s.

   a. If the ball has a constant acceleration of $-0.33\ m/s^2$, what is its velocity after 3.6 s?

   b. How far did it travel in this time?

Name ______________________

5 Chapter Assessment

4. Use the data below to make a velocity-time graph.

Time (s)	Velocity (m/s)	Time (s)	Velocity (m/s)
0.0	20.0	7.0	33.0
2.0	20.0	8.0	40.0
4.0	20.0	10.0	25.0
5.0	20.0	11.0	17.5
6.0	26.0	12.0	10.0

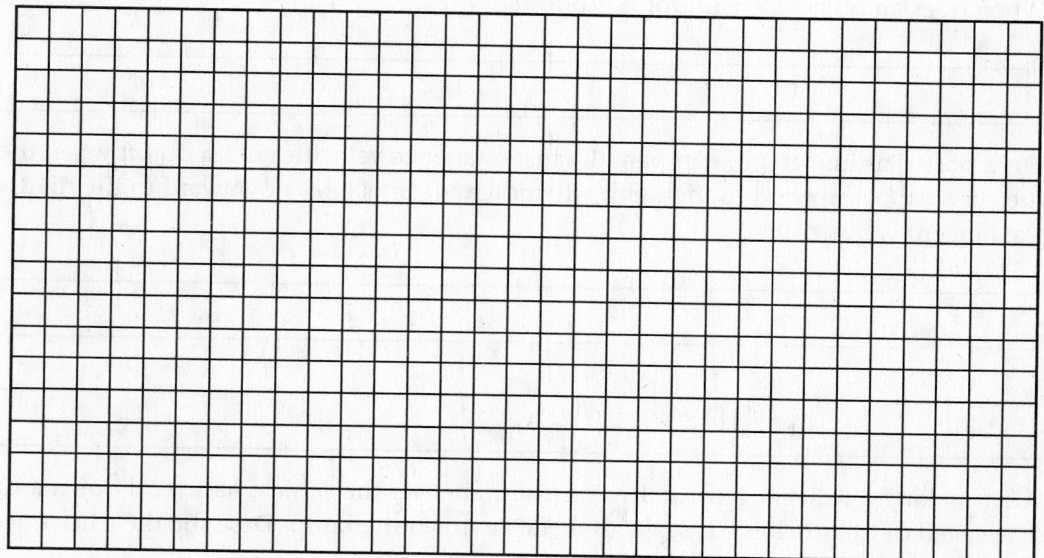

5. Describe the velocity and the acceleration of the object, using the graph you made for problem 4.

Name ______________________

5 Chapter Assessment

Applying Concepts

Answer the following questions, using complete sentences.

1. In terms of graphing, distinguish between average velocity and instantaneous velocity.

2. When does an object have uniform motion?

3. On a position-time graph, compare the instantaneous velocities of an object when the tangent to the curve slopes upward to the right, when the tangent slopes downward to the right, and when the tangent is horizontal.

4. After making a delivery, a truck driver must maneuver the vehicle backward down a narrow ramp. The speed of the truck increases with distance down the ramp. Describe the truck's acceleration.

5. How can you find the instantaneous acceleration of an object whose curve on the velocity-time graph is a straight line?

6. Suppose an object starts from rest. Explain how the displacement of the object, which has a constant acceleration, can be determined from a velocity-time graph.

7. How is the acceleration of an object in free-fall related to the acceleration due to gravity?

Name ______________________________

5 Chapter Assessment

Answer the following questions, showing your calculations.

8. Using the graph you constructed for problem 4 in Understanding Concepts Part B, determine the object's displacement after 12.0 s.

9. A toy rocket is shot straight up into the air with an initial speed of 45.0 m/s.

a. How long does it take the rocket to reach its highest point?

b. How high does the rocket rise above the ground?

Name ______________________

5 Chapter Assessment

10. A squirrel drops an acorn from a tree branch that is 8.00 m from the ground.

a. How long is the acorn in the air?

b. What is the acorn's velocity when it reaches the ground?

11. Determine how long it takes a runner moving at 10.2 m/s on a circular track to go completely around the track once. The radius of the track is 25.0 m.

Date ______________ Period ______________ Name ______________________

6 Chapter Assessment

Use with Chapter 6.

Forces

Understanding Concepts Part A

Write the letter of the choice that best completes the statement or answers the question.

_____ **1.** According to Newton's _____ law, an object with no net force acting on it remains at rest or in motion with a constant velocity.

a. first **b.** second **c.** third

_____ **2.** Losing speed as you ride your bike uphill demonstrates Newton's _____ law.

a. first **b.** second **c.** third

_____ **3.** If you push against a wall, the wall pushes back against you with _____ force.

a. no **b.** less **c.** equal **d.** more

_____ **4.** An object is in equilibrium if _____.

a. it has no weight
b. the net force on it is zero
c. it is accelerating
d. only one force is acting on it

_____ **5.** The gravitational force exerted by a large body, such as Earth, is _____.

a. weight
b. mass
c. acceleration
d. inertial mass

_____ **6.** Mass and weight are related by _____.

a. the force of gravity
b. newtons
c. friction
d. inertia

_____ **7.** If the weight of a balloon is 3000 N and the lift force provided by the atmosphere is 3300 N, in which direction is the net force acting?

a. upward
b. downward
c. toward the east
d. toward the north

_____ **8.** When the drag force on an object equals the force of gravity, the object attains _____.

a. acceleration
b. inertial mass
c. terminal velocity
d. maximum mass

_____ **9.** The period of a simple pendulum depends upon _____.

a. the mass of the bob
b. the length of the pendulum
c. the amplitude of the swing
d. the stiffness of the pendulum

_____ **10.** To produce mechanical resonance, the time between applied forces must equal the _____ of the object.

a. period
b. frequency
c. length
d. mass

Name ______________________________

6 Chapter Assessment

Understanding Concepts Part B

Answer the following questions, showing your calculations.

1. What force is required to accelerate a 6.0-kg bowling ball at +2.0 m/s^2?

2. What is the mass of a cat that weighs 30.0 N?

3. What is the tension in a rope that is supporting a 4.2-kg bucket?

4. A net force of +125 N acts on an object. Find the single force that will produce equilibrium.

5. The coefficient of sliding friction between a 78-kg box and a warehouse floor is 0.21. How much force is needed to keep the box moving at a constant velocity across the floor?

6. A 65-kg roller skater moves at a constant speed with a force of 75 N. What is the coefficient of friction between the skater and the floor of the roller rink?

Name ______________________

6 Chapter Assessment

Applying Concepts

Answer the following questions, using complete sentences.

1. Explain the relationship between mass and weight on Earth. Would this relationship change on Mars? Give a reason for your answer.

____

____

____

____

2. An elevator is traveling from the lobby to the top of a building. As it slows to a stop on the top floor, what happens to your apparent weight?

____

____

____

____

____

3. In the drawing below, use arrows to show the two horizontal and two vertical forces acting on the boat as it is pulled to the shore at a constant speed. Is there a net force on the boat?

____

____

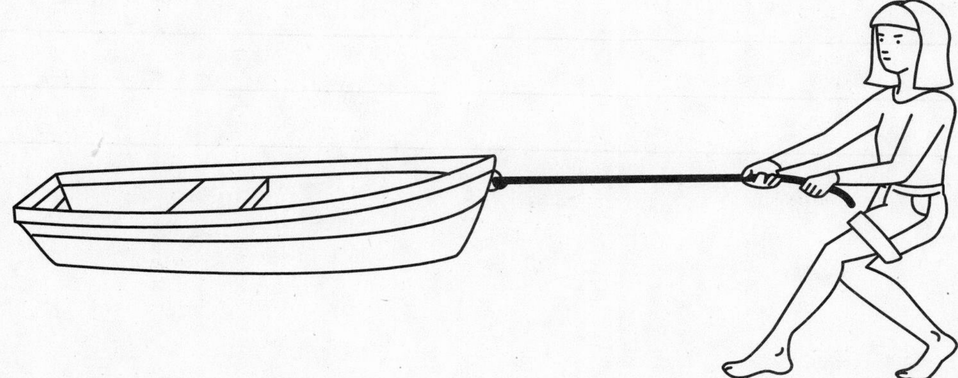

Name ______________________

6 Chapter Assessment

4. Explain what is meant by an interaction pair. Use the boat in the drawing on page 25 to give an example.

5. Suppose you pull on a rope tied to a large carton but you cannot move the carton. What forces are acting on your hand?

6. Describe the displacement, speed, and acceleration of a mass suspended on a vibrating spring as it passes through its equilibrium point.

7. Cite an example of the electromagnetic interaction as a long-range force.

Name ______________________________

6 Chapter Assessment

Answer the following questions, showing your calculations.

8. An elevator with a mass of 1.10×10^3 kg accelerates upward at 0.45 m/s^2. What is the force acting on the elevator's support cable?

9. A rocket weighs 2.0×10^7 N. Its engines exert a force of $+25 \times 10^6$ N at liftoff.

a. What is the mass of the rocket?

b. What is its acceleration when it lifts off?

c. The average acceleration of the rocket during its 7.0-min launch is 10.0 m/s^2. What velocity does it reach?

Name ______________________

6 Chapter Assessment

10. A 47-N box is pulled along a frictionless horizontal surface by a 25-N weight hanging from a cord on a frictionless pulley.

a. What is the acceleration of the box and the weight?

b. What force is exerted on the cord?

Date ______________ Period ______________ Name ______________________

7 Chapter Assessment

Use with Chapter 7.

Forces and Motion in Two Dimensions

Understanding Concepts Part A

Write the letter of the choice that best completes the statement or answers the question.

_____ **1.** The equilibrant force is _____ the resultant.

- **a.** greater than and in the same direction as
- **b.** less than but opposite in direction to
- **c.** equal in magnitude but opposite in direction to
- **d.** equal in magnitude and in the same direction as

_____ **2.** As the angle of an inclined plane increases, the parallel component of the weight force _____ and the perpendicular component of the weight force _____.

- **a.** decreases, decreases
- **b.** decreases, increases
- **c.** increases, increases
- **d.** increases, decreases

_____ **3.** The horizontal acceleration of a projectile _____ as its position changes.

- **a.** increases
- **b.** decreases
- **c.** is constant
- **d.** is zero

_____ **4.** The initial horizontal velocity of a projectile is _____ its final horizontal velocity.

a. greater than **b.** less than **c.** equal to

_____ **5.** The rising and falling times of a projectile are equal if the launching position is _____ the landing position.

a. above **b.** below **c.** at the same height as

_____ **6.** For a fast ball to pass the height of a batter's chest, the pitcher must aim the ball _____.

- **a.** exactly at the height of the batter's chest
- **b.** slightly below the height of the batter's chest
- **c.** just above the height of the batter's chest

_____ **7.** An object in circular motion travels a distance of _____ during its period.

- **a.** r
- **b.** $4\pi r^2$
- **c.** $2\pi r$
- **d.** v^2/r

_____ **8.** To start or stop rotation, the force applied to an object must _____.

- **a.** act toward the axis of rotation of the object
- **b.** be greater than the object's weight
- **c.** have a component that is perpendicular to the lever arm
- **d.** act outward from the axis of rotation of the object

Name ____________________

7 Chapter Assessment

Understanding Concepts Part B

Answer the following questions, showing your calculations.

1. A crate weighing 823 N rests on a plank that makes a 25.0° angle with the ground. Find the components of the crate's weight force parallel and perpendicular to the plank.

2. A soccer player kicks a ball into the air at an angle of 36.0° above the horizontal. The initial velocity of the ball is +30.0 m/s. How long is the soccer ball in the air?

3. What is the horizontal distance traveled by the soccer ball in problem 2?

Name ______________________

7 Chapter Assessment

4. What is the maximum height reached by the soccer ball in problem 2?

5. A runner moving at a speed of 5.6 m/s rounds a curved track with a 65 m-radius. What is the runner's centripetal acceleration?

6. A person with a mass of 75 kg sits at a distance of 1.5 m from the pivot point on a 4.0-m seesaw. Where would a person with a mass of 65 kg have to sit to balance the seesaw?

Name ______________________

7 Chapter Assessment

Applying Concepts

Answer the following questions, using complete sentences.

1. What is the relationship between the components of the weight of an object and the angle of an inclined plane on which the object rests?

2. What is the equilibrant of the perpendicular component of the weight force of a crate resting on an incline?

3. What is the equilibrant of the parallel component of the weight force of a crate resting on an incline?

4. Compare the distance a ball falls during the first second after it is dropped with the distance it falls during the second second.

5. If a ball is thrown down instead of being dropped from rest, is the average velocity for its downward motion different? Would its being thrown affect the time required to fall to the ground? Give reasons for your answers.

6. Two people are on a carnival ride that uses centripetal and frictional forces to hold its riders in place inside a rotating drum. How do the velocity, acceleration, and force acting on the people differ if one person has twice the mass of the other?

7. On a game show, contestants spin a large wheel to determine the prize associated with correct answers. How should a contestant apply force to spin the wheel as rapidly as possible?

Name ______________________________

7 Chapter Assessment

Answer the following questions, showing your calculations.

8. A 125-N sign is supported by a lightweight pole and cable as shown in the diagram. What is the tension in the cable?

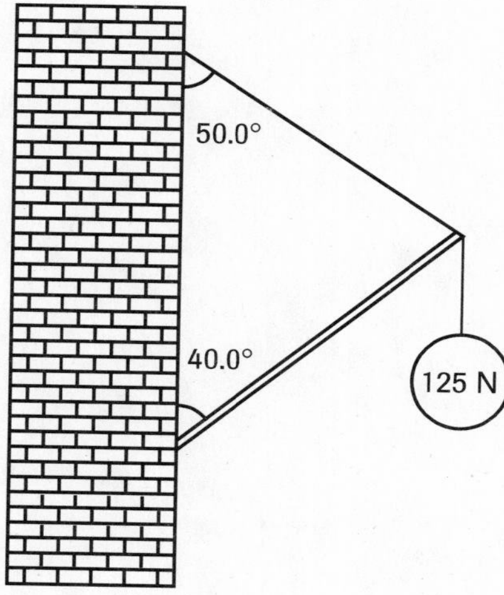

9. A 15-kg suitcase begins to slide down a luggage chute that makes an angle of 30.0° with the horizontal. The coefficient of kinetic friction for the suitcase and shoot is 0.45. What is the acceleration of the suitcase?

7 Chapter Assessment

10. A coin rolls along the top of a 1.33 m-high desk with a constant velocity. It reaches the edge of the desk and hits the ground +0.25 m from the edge of the desk. What was the velocity of the coin as it rolled across the desk?

11. A 0.050-kg disk attached to the end of a 0.150-m wire revolves uniformly on a flat, frictionless surface.

a. If the disk makes three complete revolutions per second, what is the force exerted by the wire on the object?

b. What is the speed of the disk?

Date ______________ Period ______________ Name ______________

8 Chapter Assessment

Use with Chapter 8.

Universal Gravitation

Understanding Concepts Part A

Write the letter of the choice that best completes each statement.

______ **1.** During its orbital period, as a planet moves closer to the sun, the orbital velocity of the planet _____.

a. increases **b.** decreases **c.** remains the same

______ **2.** According to Newton's law of universal gravitation, the force of attraction between any two masses is directly related to the _____.

a. distance between the masses
b. product of the two masses
c. velocity of the two masses
d. sum of the two masses

______ **3.** As the distance between two bodies increases, the force of attraction between the bodies _____.

a. increases **b.** decreases **c.** remains the same

______ **4.** Astronauts in an orbiting space shuttle experience a sensation of weightlessness because _____.

a. the space shuttle is falling freely toward Earth
b. the space shuttle is not affected by Earth's gravity
c. the mass of the space shuttle decreases as the distance from Earth increases
d. the space shuttle is moving away from Earth

______ **5.** Anything that has mass is surrounded by a _____.

a. satellite in orbit
b. magnetic field
c. gravitational field
d. black hole

______ **6.** The force of gravity exerts a _____ on an orbiting satellite.

a. balanced force
b. centripetal force
c. tangential force
d. All these are true.

______ **7.** The pair of spheres that experiences the greatest force of attraction is _____.

a. A and B
b. B and C
c. A and C

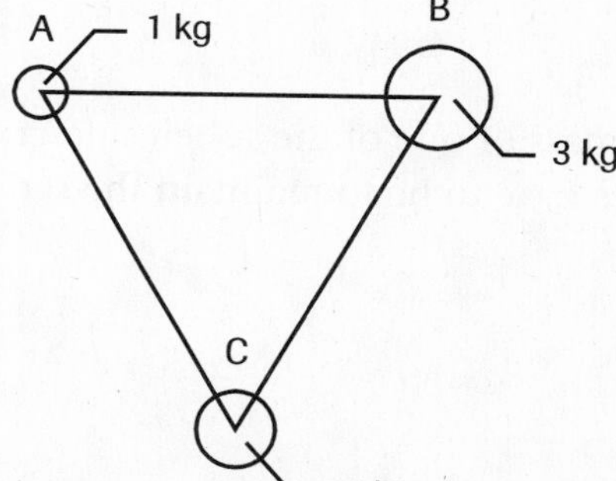

Name ____________________

8 Chapter Assessment

Understanding Concepts Part B

Answer the following questions, showing your calculations.

1. Which of the pairs of masses below will have the greatest force of attraction between the spheres?

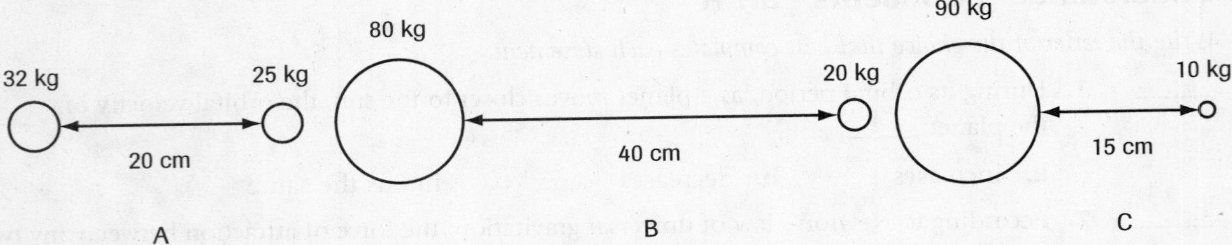

2. Two spheres, each having a mass of 20.0 kg, are positioned so that their centers are 8.00 m apart. What is the gravitational force between the spheres?

3. What will the force be if the spheres described in problem 2 are positioned with their centers 4.00 m apart?

4. If the mass of one of the spheres described in problem 2 were doubled, how far apart would the spheres have to be to maintain the same gravitational force between them?

Name ____________________

8 Chapter Assessment

Applying Concepts

Answer the following questions, using complete sentences.

1. Explain why Kepler was able to use Tycho Brahe's data about the positions of stars and planets to develop his laws of planetary motion, while Brahe was unable to use the same data successfully.

2. Earth is closer to the sun in December than it is in July. What happens to the orbital speed of the planet between July and December? Explain your answer.

3. What would happen to the magnitude of the gravitational force between two bodies if:

a. the mass of one of the bodies were doubled?

b. the distance between the two bodies were doubled?

4. What information do you need to find the period of a planet using Kepler's third law?

5. The mass of Jupiter is approximately 318 times that of Earth. Yet the surface gravity of Jupiter is less than three times the surface gravity of Earth. How do you account for this apparent discrepancy?

6. How does an artificial satellite remain in orbit at a constant distance from Earth's surface?

7. How does Einstein's general theory of relativity account for the blackness of black holes in the universe?

Name ______________________

8 Chapter Assessment

Answer the following questions, showing your calculations.

8. The distance between Earth and the sun is often expressed as 1 astronomical unit (AU). Using this unit, find the distance between the sun and Mars, which has a period of approximately 686 Earth days.

9. The mean distance between the center of Earth and the center of the moon is 3.84×10^8 m, and the moon has an orbital period of 27.3 days. Find the distance from Earth of an artificial satellite that has an orbital period of 9.1 days.

10. The gravitational force between two spheres is 2.50×10^{-8} N. Their centers are 105 cm apart. The smaller sphere has a mass of 8.2 kg. Find the mass of the larger sphere.

11. A body orbits the sun at a distance ten times the mean distance of Earth's orbit from the sun. The sun's mass is 1.99×10^{30} kg, and its distance from Earth is 1.50×10^{11} m.

a. Find the period of the body in years.

b. Determine the speed of the body.

Date ______________ Period ______________ Name ______________________

9 Chapter Assessment

Use with Chapter 9.

Momentum and Its Conservation

Understanding Concepts Part A

Write the letter of the choice that best completes the statement or answers the question.

_____ **1.** The linear momentum of an object can be calculated by multiplying the mass of the object by its _____.

a. acceleration
b. velocity
c. impulse
d. time

_____ **2.** The greatest change in momentum will be produced by a _____.

a. large force acting over a long time
b. small force acting over a short time
c. large force acting over a short time

_____ **3.** Impulse can be represented by _____.

a. $\Delta v/\Delta t$
b. $F\Delta t$
c. mv
d. m/v

_____ **4.** When a golf club hits a golf ball, the change in momentum of the ball is _____ the change in momentum of the club.

a. equal to **b.** greater than **c.** less than

_____ **5.** A system is closed if _____.

a. no net external force acts on it
b. the momentum of each object in the system remains constant
c. the system does not gain or lose mass
d. objects can enter, but not leave, the system

_____ **6.** An internal force _____ the total momentum of a closed system.

a. increases **b.** decreases **c.** does not change

_____ **7.** A person is standing on roller blades and is holding a heavy medicine ball. If he throws the medicine ball horizontally to the right, what will be his resulting motion?

a. to the right
b. to the left
c. backward
d. no motion

_____ **8.** Two moving objects collide and move on paths that are 120° apart. The total momentum of the objects after the collision is _____ the total momentum before the collision.

a. equal to **b.** greater than **c.** less than

Name ______________________

9 Chapter Assessment

Understanding Concepts Part B

Answer the following questions, showing your calculations.

1. What is the momentum of a 145-g baseball traveling at +40.0 m/s?

2. What impulse is needed to stop a 45-g mass traveling at a velocity of –42 m/s?

3. A force with a magnitude of 540 N is used to stop an object with a mass of 65 kg moving at a velocity of +175 m/s. How long will it take to bring the object to a full stop?

4. In hitting a stationary hockey puck having a mass of 180 g, a hockey player gives the puck an impulse of 6.0 N·s. At what speed will the puck move toward the goal?

Name ______________________

9 Chapter Assessment

5. A metal sphere with a mass of 80.0 g rolls along a frictionless surface at 20.0 m/s and strikes a stationary sphere having a mass of 200.0 g. The first sphere stops completely. At what speed does the second sphere move away from the point of impact?

6. A snowball with a mass of 85 g hits a snowman's top hat and sticks to it. The hat and the snowball, with a combined mass of 220 g, fall off together at 8.0 m/s. How fast was the snowball moving at the moment of impact?

Name ______________________________

9 Chapter Assessment

Applying Concepts

Answer the following questions, using complete sentences.

1. Explain how a motorcycle can have the same linear momentum as an automobile.

____

____

____

2. To bunt a baseball effectively, at the instant the ball strikes the bat, the batter moves the bat in the same direction as the moving baseball. What effect does this action have? Why?

____

____

____

____

____

____

3. In the sport of curling, players slide 19-kg masses called stones along the surface of the ice toward a target. If a stone traveling 3 m/s strikes a stationary stone directly, the first stone will stop moving. Using the concept of conservation of momentum, describe what happens to the second stone. Assume there is no friction.

____

____

4. Why does a fire hose recoil when the water is turned on?

____

____

____

____

____

5. Suppose you were an astronaut drifting in space several meters from your spacecraft. The only thing you have with you is a sack filled with moon rocks. How could you return to your ship?

____

____

____

____

Name ______________________

9 Chapter Assessment

Answer the following questions, showing your calculations.

6. A ball with a mass of 12 g moving at +15.0 m/s collides with a second ball with a mass of 36 g moving at +5.0 m/s. After the collision, the 12-g ball moves at +6.0 m/s. What is the change in momentum of the 36-g ball?

7. A 24.0-kg dog running at a speed of 3.0 m/s jumps onto a stationary skateboard that has a mass of 3.6 kg. How long will it take an average force with a magnitude 9.0 N to stop the skateboard and dog?

Name ______________________________

9 Chapter Assessment

8. A sphere of mass 5.00 kg moving at 4.00 m/s collides with an identical sphere that is at rest. The first sphere moves off at an angle of 60.0° to the left of its original path, and the second sphere moves off in a direction 90.0° to the right of the first sphere's final path. What are the speeds of the two spheres as they separate? Assume frictionless conditions.

Date ________ Period ________ Name ________

10 Chapter Assessment

Use with Chapter 10.

Energy, Work, and Simple Machines

Understanding Concepts Part A

Write the letter of the choice that best completes the statement or answers the question.

_____ **1.** Any object that has energy has the ability to _____.

a. burn **b.** produce a change **c.** fall

_____ **2.** If the environment does work on a system, _____.

a. the environment warms

b. the energy of the system increases

c. the energy of the system decreases

d. the quantity of work done on the system has a negative value

_____ **3.** When a force is exerted on an object, work is done only if the object _____.

a. is heavy **c.** moves

b. remains stationary **d.** has no momentum

_____ **4.** In which of the following situations is no work done on a football?

a. picking up the football **c.** dropping the football

b. carrying the football down the field

_____ **5.** In which of the following situations is work done on the football by a person?

a. picking up the football **c.** dropping the football

b. carrying the football down the field

_____ **6.** In which of the following situations is work done on the football by gravity?

a. picking up the football **c.** dropping the football

b. carrying the football down the field

Write the term that correctly completes each statement.

7. One definition of ________ is "work done per unit time."

8. A machine with a mechanical advantage greater than 1 increases ________.

9. For an ideal machine, efficiency is always ________ percent.

10. If the mechanical advantage of a machine is less than 1, effort force is ________ than resistance force.

11. A wedge used to split wood is a ________ machine.

12. A pair of gears make up a ________ machine.

Name ______________________________

10 Chapter Assessment

Understanding Concepts Part B

Answer the following questions, showing your calculations.

1. How much work is done if you raise a 6.0-N weight 1.5 m above the ground?

2. Using an ideal machine, a worker exerts an effort force of 5.0 N to lift a 12.0-N weight a distance of 3.0 m. How far does the effort force move?

3. An effort force of 200.0 N is applied to an ideal machine to move a 750.0-N resistance a distance of 300.0 cm. What is the mechanical advantage of the machine?

4. How much power is developed by an electric motor that moves a 500-N load a distance of 20 m in 10 s?

5. What is the efficiency of a machine that requires a work input of 190 J to achieve a work output of 160 J?

6. How much power is generated by a machine in lifting 250 kg a distance of 150 m in 30.0 s?

Name ______________________

10 Chapter Assessment

Applying Concepts

Answer the following questions, using complete sentences.

1. Two students are moving 80-N cartons of books from the floor onto a platform. One student moves 12 cartons in 7 minutes. The other student moves the same number of cartons in 5 minutes. Which student does more work? Explain your answer.

____

____

____

2. What type of simple machine is the handle of a pencil sharpener? How does it make work easier?

____

____

3. If a machine is used to increase force, what factor is sacrificed? Cite an example.

____

____

____

____

4. Distinguish between work and power.

____

____

5. Explain the following: When a screwdriver is used to drive a screw, the diameter of its handle is more important than its length, but when used to pry open a stuck window, its length is more important than the diameter of its handle.

____

____

____

____

6. Use mechanical advantage to explain what happens when you shift the gears of a multispeed bike.

____

____

____

____

Name ______________________________

10 Chapter Assessment

Answer the following questions, showing your calculations.

7. An adult and a child exert a total force of 930 N in pushing a car 15 m down their driveway. The adult exerts twice as much force as the child. How much work does each person do?

8. An adult exerts a force of 26 N to pull a child across the snow on a sled. The rope that joins the sled at an angle of 30.0° above horizontal. Ignoring friction, how much work is done in pulling the sled 390 m?

9. A grocer lifts an 8.0-kg carton from the floor to a height of 0.80 m, carries it 24 m across the store, and places it on a shelf 1.8 m above the floor. How much work does the grocer accomplish?

10. At what speed can a 150-W motor lift a 2500-N load?

11. A mover pushes a 260-kg piano on wheels up a ramp 7.0 m long onto a stage 1.75 m above the auditorium floor. The mover pushes the piano with a force of 680 N.

a. How much work does the mover do?

b. What work is done on the piano by the machine?

c. What is the efficiency of the machine?

Date ______________ Period ______________ Name ______________________

11 Chapter Assessment

Use with Chapter 11.

Energy

Understanding Concepts Part A

For each of the statements below, write true *or rewrite the italicized part to make the statement true.*

1. When you throw a ball into the air, its mechanical energy at any point is the *difference* in its kinetic energy and gravitational potential energy.

____

2. As an object falls towards Earth, the gravitational potential energy of the object *increases.*

____

3. The total amount of energy in an isolated, closed system *remains constant.*

____

4. If a tabletop is used as a reference point in a mechanical-energy problem, an object lying on the tabletop has a gravitational potential energy *greater than zero.*

____

5. Of the three sets of bar graphs below, an inelastic collision is represented by *set A.*

____

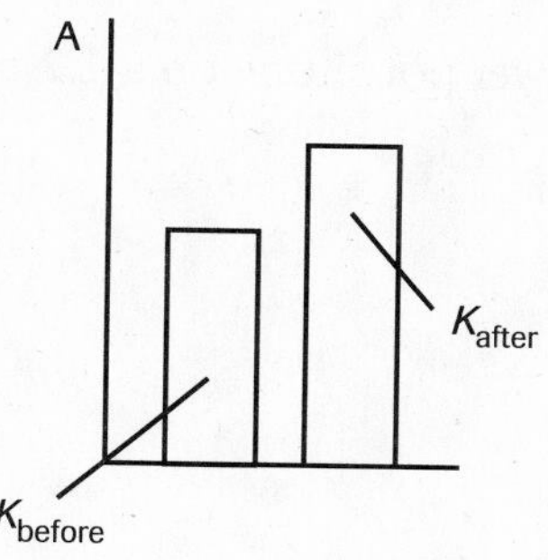

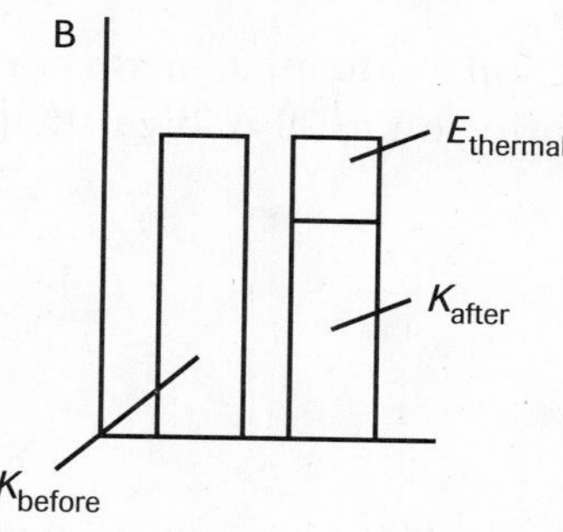

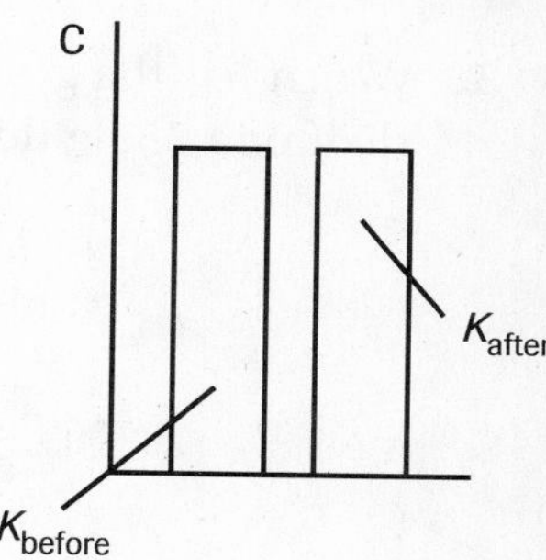

For each term on the left, write the letter of the matching item.

_____ **6.** K

_____ **7.** U_g

_____ **8.** 1 joule

_____ **9.** work-energy theorem

_____ **10.** result of an elastic collision

a. $K_{after} = K_{before}$

b. $= mgh$

c. $= \frac{1}{2} mv^2$

d. $1\ kg \cdot m^2/s^2$

e. $Fd = \Delta K$

Name ______________________

11 Chapter Assessment

Understanding Concepts Part B

Answer the following questions, showing your calculations.

1. Determine the mechanical energy of a 5.0-kg stone perched near the edge of a cliff 25.0 m high. Use the base of the cliff as the reference level.

2. Compare the kinetic energies of a biker and bike (with a combined mass of 80 kg) traveling at 3.00 m/s and the same biker and bike traveling twice as fast.

3. Which has the greater gravitational potential energy—a 550-g flower pot sitting on a 1.2-m high shelf or a 350-g flower pot sitting on a 1.8-m high shelf?

4. A weight trainer lifts a 90.0-kg barbell from a stand 0.90 m high and raises it to a height of 1.75 m. What is the increase in the potential energy of the barbell?

5. A child having a mass of 35.0 kg is on a sled having a mass of 5.0 kg. If the child and sled traveling together have a kinetic energy of 260 J, how fast are they moving?

Name ____________________

11 Chapter Assessment

Applying Concepts

Answer the following questions, using complete sentences.

1. Describe the energy changes that take place when the spring of a toy car is wound up and then released.

2. Why must the first hill of a roller-coaster ride be the highest hill?

3. Distinguish between an elastic collision and an inelastic collision.

4. A ball is thrown upward. Describe changes in its mechanical energy, kinetic energy, and gravitational potential energy between the time the ball is released and the time it reaches its maximum height.

Name ______________________

11 Chapter Assessment

5. A block of wood rests on a frictionless surface and is attached to a spring, as shown below. When the spring is neither elongated nor compressed, the center of the block of wood is used as the reference point for the elastic potential energy of the block-and-spring system. The spring is then compressed to the left and released. Describe changes in the mechanical energy, kinetic energy, and elastic potential energy of the system between the time the spring is released and when it reaches its maximum elongation.

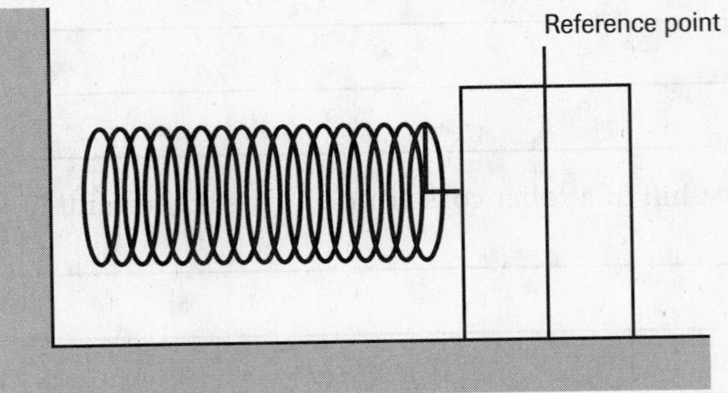

Name ______________________

11 Chapter Assessment

Answer the following questions, showing your calculations.

6. Under what conditions will a 0.030-kg marble and a 3.00-kg rock have the same gravitational potential energy other than zero?

7. Under what conditions will a moving 0.030-kg marble and a moving 3.00-kg rock have the same kinetic energy?

8. During a contest that involved throwing a 7.0-kg bowling ball straight up in the air, one contestant exerted a force of 810 N on the ball. If the force was exerted through a distance of 2.0 m, how high did the ball go from the point of release?

Name ______________________

11 Chapter Assessment

9. A 50.0-kg girl jumps onto a stationary 2.4-kg skateboard at 4.1 m/s. Determine the fraction of the original kinetic energy that was lost due to the inelastic nature of the collision.

10. A 50.0-kg skater and skateboard leaves the right side of the ramp shown below at a speed of 7.0 m/s. If the ramp is frictionless, what was his initial speed down the opposite side of the ramp?

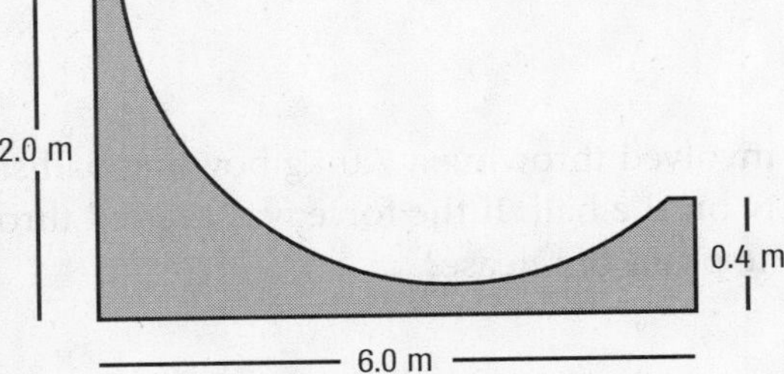

Date ______________ Period ______________ Name ______________________

12 Chapter Assessment

Use with Chapter 12.

Thermal Energy

Understanding Concepts Part A

Write the letter of the choice that best completes each statement.

_____ **1.** The measure of the hotness of an object is its _____.
- **a.** entropy
- **b.** heat of vaporization
- **c.** specific heat
- **d.** temperature

_____ **2.** The amount of heat needed to melt 1 kg of a substance is the _____.
- **a.** heat of fusion
- **b.** entropy
- **c.** heat of vaporization
- **d.** specific heat

_____ **3.** A heat engine continuously converts _____.
- **a.** mechanical energy to thermal energy
- **b.** thermal energy to mechanical energy
- **c.** entropy to thermal energy
- **d.** heat to temperature

_____ **4.** Entropy is the measure of a system's _____.
- **a.** disorder
- **b.** temperature
- **c.** thermal energy
- **d.** thermal equilibrium

_____ **5.** Energy that flows as a result of a difference in temperature is called _____.
- **a.** entropy
- **b.** heat
- **c.** kinetic energy
- **d.** specific heat

_____ **6.** Two objects are in thermal equilibrium if they _____.
- **a.** contain the same number of particles
- **b.** have the same thermal energy
- **c.** are at the same temperature
- **d.** have the same entropy

For each of the statements below, write true *or* false.

7. ____________________ According to the second law of thermodynamics, natural processes go in a direction that maintains or increases the total entropy of the universe.

8. ____________________ The total increase in the thermal energy of a system is the work done on it minus the heat added to it.

9. ____________________ A heat pump is a refrigerator that can be run in two directions.

10. ____________________ An increase in the average kinetic energy of particles means an increase in temperature.

11. ____________________ Convection typically takes place in solids.

12. ____________________ A thermometer is used to measure heat.

Name ______________________

12 Chapter Assessment

Understanding Concepts Part B

Answer the following questions, showing your calculations.

1. Helium has the lowest boiling point of all elements. It boils at −269°C. Express that temperature in kelvins.

2. The specific heat of methanol is 2450 J/kg·K. Calculate the amount of heat that must be added to 0.25 kg of methanol to raise its temperature by 15°C.

3. Ice has a specific heat of 2060 J/kg·K. How much heat must be absorbed by 2.0 kg of ice at −20.0°C to raise it up to 0.0°C, before any melting actually takes place?

4. Given that ice has a heat of fusion of 3.34×10^5 J/kg, how much more heat must be added to the ice in problem 3 to change it to liquid water at 0.0°C?

5. The heat of vaporization of water is 2.26×10^6 J/kg. How much heat must be added to 1.5 kg of liquid water at 100°C to change it to steam at the same temperature?

6. Iron has a heat of fusion of 2.66×10^5 J/kg. How much heat must be removed from 7.94 kg of molten iron at its freezing point to turn it into solid iron at the same temperature?

Name ________________________

12 Chapter Assessment

Applying Concepts

Answer the following questions, using complete sentences.

1. Distinguish between thermal energy, temperature, and heat.

2. Explain what is meant by the kinetic-molecular theory and how it applies to the study of thermal energy.

3. Explain what is meant by absolute zero. What is its value on the Celsius scale and on the Kelvin scale?

4. Equal masses of methanol and liquid water initially at the same temperature are heated by the same heat source. The specific heat of methanol is 2450 J/kg·K, and that of water is 4180 J/kg·K. Compare the temperatures of these two substances after they are heated for the same period of time. Give a reason for your answer.

5. A sample of iron at a temperature of 225 K is placed in a container of water at a temperature of 350 K. Describe what will take place in terms of heat transfer and temperature.

6. How does the entropy of a system change when heat is removed from the system?

Name ____________________

12 Chapter Assessment

Answer the following questions, showing your calculations.

7. A 4.0-kg iron ball at 225°C is placed in a container of liquid water at 4°C. When the system reaches thermal equilibrium, its temperature is 45°C. What is the mass of water in the container? The specific heat of iron is 450 J/kg·K, and the specific heat of water is 4180 J/kg·K.

8. A 2.0-kg cube of iron at 300.0°C is placed on a 5-kg block of ice at 0.0°C. How much ice will change to liquid water at 0.0°C? The specific heat of iron is 450 J/kg·K, and the heat of fusion of ice is 3.34×10^5 J/kg.

9. How much heat is absorbed in changing 2.00 kg of ice at –5.0°C to steam at 110.0°C? The specific heats of ice, liquid water, and steam are, respectively, 2060 J/kg·K, 4180 J/kg·K, and 2020 J/kg·K. The heat of fusion of ice is 3.34×10^5 J/kg. The heat of vaporization of water is 2.26×10^6 J/kg.

10. How much heat must be added to 1.5 kg of liquid water at 95.0°C to change it to steam at 100.0°C? The specific heat of liquid water is 4180 J/kg·K. The heat of vaporization of water is 2.26×10^6 J/kg.

Date ________________ Period ________________ Name ________________________________

13 Chapter Assessment

Use with Chapter 13.

States of Matter

Understanding Concepts Part A

Write the letter of the choice that best completes the statement or answers the question.

_____ **1.** At sea level, if the area of a surface increases, the pressure of the atmosphere on the surface _____.

a. increases **b.** decreases **c.** stays the same

_____ **2.** Pressure is equal to _____.

a. force plus area
b. force times area
c. force minus area
d. force divided by area

_____ **3.** The SI unit of pressure is the _____.

a. pascal **b.** atmosphere **c.** millibar **d.** newton

_____ **4.** According to Pascal's principle, any change on a confined fluid _____.

a. is directly proportional to the volume of the fluid
b. is inversely proportional to the volume of the fluid
c. depends on the shape of the container
d. is transmitted unchanged throughout the fluid

_____ **5.** The buoyant force exerted on an object immersed in a fluid is equal to the _____.

a. volume of the displaced fluid
b. weight of the displaced fluid
c. weight of the immersed object
d. mass of the immersed object

_____ **6.** According to Bernoulli's principle, as the velocity of a fluid increases, the _____.

a. density of the fluid decreases
b. pressure exerted by the fluid decreases
c. mass of the fluid increases
d. buoyant force of the fluid decreases

For each of the statements below, write true *or rewrite the italicized part to make the statement true.*

7. ______________________ As heat is applied to a sample of liquid water at 1°C, the volume of the water *decreases*.

8. ______________________ A crystal lattice is a characteristic of many *gases*.

9. ______________________ An object that is deformed by a force and returns to its original form when the force is removed is exhibiting the property of *elasticity*.

10. ______________________ The *liquid* state is the state of matter in which electrons have been torn away from the atoms.

11. ______________________ The *adhesive* forces within a liquid account for surface tension.

Name ______________________

13 Chapter Assessment

Understanding Concepts Part B

Answer the following questions, showing your calculations.

1. Atmospheric pressure at sea level is about 1.0×10^5 Pa. How much force does the atmosphere exert on a driveway that is 18.0 m long and 5.0 m wide?

2. Find the total force exerted by Earth's atmosphere on the top and sides of a rectangular can. The base of the can is 10.0 cm wide and 15.0 cm long, and the can is 12.0 cm high.

3. A force of 400.0 N is exerted on a small piston that has an area of 8.0 cm^2. How much weight can be lifted on a large piston to which the force is transmitted, given that the large piston has an area of 20.0 cm^2?

4. The area of a small piston is 4.0 cm^2. A force of 150 N on the small piston will move a weight of 1200 N on a large piston. What is the area of the large piston?

Name ______________________

13 Chapter Assessment

5. A cube of lead that is 10.0 cm on each edge is suspended from a line and immersed in water. How much force is exerted on the line holding the lead cube? The density of lead is 11.3×10^3 kg/m^3.

6. An iron bar 1.6 m long at room temperature (20°C) is heated uniformly along its entire length until its temperature reaches 1250°C. How much longer is the bar at the higher temperature? The coefficient of linear expansion of iron is 1.2×10^{-5} (°C)$^{-1}$.

Name ______________________

13 Chapter Assessment

Applying Concepts

Answer the following questions, using complete sentences.

1. What does the kinetic-molecular theory of matter say about gases?

2. Most automobile brake systems are hydraulic systems. Explain how the relatively small force involved in pressing on a brake pedal can give the brakes enough force to stop the car.

3. An iron cube weighing 5 N is suspended from a string and lowered into a container of water until the cube is completely immersed. Describe what seems to happen to the weight of the cube. Give a reason for your answer.

Name ______________________

13 Chapter Assessment

4. What properties can be used to distinguish between gases and liquids? What properties do gases and liquids have in common that allow them to be classified as fluids?

5. How is matter in the plasma state similar to matter in the gas state? How is it different?

6. Explain the principle behind the operation of a bimetallic strip.

Name ______________________________

13 Chapter Assessment

Answer the following questions, showing your calculations.

7. A cylindrical water tank 20.0 m high has a diameter of 14.0 m. The tank is full of water. What is the pressure at the bottom of the tank?

8. A rectangular solid measures 1.20 m by 0.80 m by 0.20 m. When the solid is standing on its smallest face, it exerts a pressure of 5.2×10^3 Pa. How much does the solid weigh?

9. What is the density of the solid in problem 8?

10. A volume of 200.0 cm^3 of water at a temperature of 4°C is in a container with a 1000-cm^3 capacity. The container and its contents are heated to 95°C. What is the final volume of water in the container? The coefficient of volume expansion of water is $210 \times 10^{-6}(°C)^{-1}$.

Date ______________ Period ______________ Name ______________________

14 Chapter Assessment

Use with Chapter 14.

Waves and Energy Transfer

Understanding Concepts Part A

Write the letter of the choice that best completes the statement or answers the question.

_____ **1.** Which of the following usually transmits energy without transferring matter?
a. particle **b.** electron **c.** wave **d.** proton

_____ **2.** The time interval during which wave motion repeats is the _____.
a. wave pulse **b.** frequency **c.** period **d.** wavelength

_____ **3.** The number of vibrations per second is the _____.
a. amplitude **b.** frequency **c.** period **d.** wavelength

_____ **4.** The speed of any mechanical wave depends on _____.
a. the medium through which it travels **c.** its angle of reflection
b. its amplitude **d.** its energy

_____ **5.** When light from the air enters a body of water, in what form does some of the energy move back into the air?
a. reflected wave **c.** incident wave
b. transmitted wave **d.** sound wave

_____ **6.** Which of the following may be produced during destructive interference of waves?
a. a reflection **c.** a node
b. a higher crest **d.** a lower trough

_____ **7.** The change in wave direction at the boundary of two different media is _____.
a. incidence **b.** refraction **c.** reflection **d.** diffraction

_____ **8.** The spreading of waves around the edge of a barrier is _____.
a. incidence **b.** refraction **c.** reflection **d.** diffraction

For each of the statements below, write true *or rewrite the italicized part to make the statement true.*

9. ______________________ Increasing the amplitude of a wave *decreases* the rate of energy transfer.

10. ______________________ Frequency is *inversely* related to period.

11. ______________________ Wavelength is measured in *hertz.*

12. ______________________ Wave speed equals *frequency* times wavelength.

13. ______________________ The *node* is a line at a right angle to the barrier.

Name ______________________

14 Chapter Assessment

Understanding Concepts Part B

Answer the following questions, showing your calculations.

1. A note on a piano vibrates 262 times per second. What is the period of the wave?

2. If sound travels at 5600 m/s through a steel rod, what is the wavelength, given a wave frequency of 2480 Hz?

3. What is the speed of a wave that has a frequency of 3.7×10^3 Hz and a wavelength of 1.2×10^{-2} m?

4. A beam of light strikes a mirror, making an angle of 43° relative to the normal. What is the angle between the normal and the reflected ray?

5. The wavelength of a water wave is 4.0×10^2 m. The wave is approaching land at 25 m/s. What is the period?

6. The wavelength of a sound produced by a tuning fork is 1.30 m. The fork has a frequency of 256 Hz. What is the wave velocity?

Name ______________________

14 Chapter Assessment

Applying Concepts

Answer the following questions, using complete sentences.

1. Describe the relationship between the amplitude of a wave and the energy that is transferred by the wave.

2. Suppose two boats are a few meters apart and lie along a line perpendicular to the shore. Describe their motion if they are subjected to passing ocean waves whose wavelength is not equal to the distance between the boats. Will the oscillations of the two boats have the same amplitudes and frequencies?

3. Contrast the reflection of a wave that passes from one medium into a lighter, more flexible medium to a wave that passes from one medium into a heavier and stiffer medium.

4. What is the principle of superposition, and how is it related to interference?

5. Describe a standing wave and explain how it can be produced.

6. Describe what occurs if waves pass through two closely spaced holes in a barrier.

Name ______________________

14 Chapter Assessment

Answer the following questions, showing your calculations.

7. Suppose you set a cup of milk on the kitchen counter while the dishwasher is running. You notice that the vibration of the dishwasher causes standing waves in the milk. The crests of the waves form four concentric rings. The radius of the cup is 3.0 cm, and the speed of the wave in the liquid is 1.5 m/s. What is the frequency of the vibrations coming from the dishwasher? (Hint: Think in terms of how many wavelengths lie along the radius.)

8. The average distance between Earth and the moon is 384 790 km. If Earth's atmosphere were uniform and extended to the moon's surface, how many seconds would it take sound to travel from Earth to the moon? How many days would that equal? Assume that the speed of sound is 343 m/s.

9. Waves traveling along a long string are reflected from the fixed end. They produce a standing wave that has a wavelength of 2.4 m. How far from the fixed end are the first two antinodes? Note that there is a node at the fixed end.

____

____

____

____

10. Two dissimilar springs are tied together. A wave is started on the first spring. The wavelength is 0.20 m, and the speed is 5.0 m/s. When the wave reaches the second spring, it moves along that spring at a speed of 7.5 m/s. What is the wavelength of the wave in the second spring?

Date ______________ Period ______________ Name ______________________

15 Chapter Assessment

Use with Chapter 15.

Sound

Understanding Concepts Part A

Write the letter of the choice that best completes the statement or answers the question.

_____ **1.** Echoes demonstrate which behavior of sound waves?
a. refraction **b.** diffraction **c.** interference **d.** reflection

_____ **2.** Sound is an example of what kind of wave?
a. transverse **b.** electromagnetic **c.** longitudinal **d.** surface

_____ **3.** As an approaching ambulance passes an unmoving observer, what happens to the apparent pitch of the sound emitted by the ambulance siren, as heard by the observer?
a. It increases. **c.** It decreases.
b. It stays the same. **d.** It becomes inaudible.

_____ **4.** A detected apparent change in the pitch caused by the motion of a sound source or of an observer is called _____.
a. refraction **c.** reflection
b. the Doppler shift **d.** diffraction

_____ **5.** The pitch of a sound depends most directly upon the sound's _____.
a. frequency **b.** speed **c.** amplitude **d.** loudness

_____ **6.** If two notes have a frequency ratio of 1:2, the notes differ by a(n) _____.
a. major third **b.** fifth **c.** octave **d.** fourth

_____ **7.** If two notes have a frequency ratio of 2:3, the notes differ by a(n) _____.
a. major third **b.** fifth **c.** octave **d.** fourth

_____ **8.** Approximately how many times greater is the pressure amplitude of a 40-dB sound than that of a 20-dB sound?
a. 5 **b.** 20 **c.** 10 **d.** 100

For each of the statements below, write true *or* false.

9. ______________________ The outermost structure of the human ear that is used to collect sound waves is called the cochlea.

10. ______________________ Tone quality or tone color is also called timbre.

11. ______________________ For an open-pipe resonator, a column of length $\frac{1}{2}$ will resonate with a tuning fork.

12. ______________________ The frequency of a beat is the sum of the frequencies of the two waves that produce it.

Name ______________________

15 Chapter Assessment

Understanding Concepts Part B

Answer the following questions, showing your calculations.

1. A sound wave traveling at a speed of 340.0 m/s has a wavelength of 1.25 m. What is the frequency of the sound?

2. How long is a wave that has the same frequency as the one in problem 1 and that is traveling through water at 1435 m/s?

3. A note on the piano has a frequency of 55 Hz. What is the frequency of the note that is three octaves higher?

4. What is the wavelength of a sound made by a violin string vibrating at 640 Hz if the wave is traveling at 350 m/s?

5. What is the period of the sound wave in problem 4?

6. A 448-Hz tuning fork and a 444-Hz tuning fork are struck at the same time. What is the frequency of the beat produced?

7. Two tuning forks struck simultaneously produce a beat with a frequency of 2 Hz. The frequency of one fork is 364 Hz. What are the two possible frequencies of the other tuning fork?

Name ______________________

15 Chapter Assessment

Applying Concepts

Answer the following questions, using complete sentences.

1. In terms of resonance, pitch, and frequency, describe how sound is produced in a trumpet.

____

____

____

2. How do molecules in air allow a distant listener to hear a trumpet?

____

____

____

3. Explain how and why the apparent pitch of a whistle of a moving train is different for a person standing on the platform ahead of the train, for a person standing behind the train, and for a person on the train.

____

____

____

____

____

____

____

4. Contrast the harmonics of open-pipe resonators with the harmonics of closed-pipe resonators.

____

____

____

____

5. Describe the decibel scale and its relationship to actual pressure amplitude and perceived loudness.

____

____

____

____

Name ______________________________

15 Chapter Assessment

Answer the following questions, showing your calculations.

6. The speed of sound through air depends on air temperature. At 20°C, sound waves travel through air at 343 m/s. What is the temperature of the air if the speed of sound is 351 m/s? Assume that the velocity of sound in air increases 0.60 m/s for each increase of 1°C.

7. A tuning fork has a frequency of 365 Hz. In an air column, the fork causes the loudest sounds at resonant lengths that are separated by 45.6 cm. What is the velocity of the sound? Recall that resonance lengths are spaced by half-wavelength intervals.

8 A tuning fork with a frequency of 365 Hz is held above an air column. What is the spacing between resonant lengths if the air temperature is 15°C? Assume that the speed of sound in air changes by 0.60 m/s for each 1°C change of temperature.

9. A note has a frequency of 326 Hz. What is the frequency of a note that is one octave lower? What is the frequency of a note that is a fifth higher than the note?

Date ______________ Period ______________ Name ______________________

16 Chapter Assessment

Use with Chapter 16.

Light

Understanding Concepts Part A

Write the letter of the choice that best completes the statement or answers the question.

_____ **1.** What kind of wave is light?
a. electromagnetic **b.** mechanical **c.** surface **d.** longitudinal

_____ **2.** The wavelength of red light is approximately _____.
a. 200 nm **b.** 400 nm **c.** 500 nm **d.** 700 nm

_____ **3.** Which of the following characteristics of light has a defined value?
a. wavelength **c.** frequency
b. speed in a vacuum **d.** amplitude

_____ **4.** The rate, in lumens, at which light is emitted from a lightbulb is the bulb's _____.
a. luminous flux **c.** frequency
b. illuminance **d.** luminous intensity

_____ **5.** Illumination under a small light source is proportional to _____.
a. r **b.** r^2 **c.** $1/r$ **d.** $1/r^2$

_____ **6.** Very thin white tissue paper can best be described as _____.
a. transparent **b.** translucent **c.** opaque **d.** luminous

_____ **7** Materials that do not allow any transmission of light are described as _____.
a. transparent **b.** translucent **c.** opaque **d.** luminous

_____ **8.** What kind of process is the mixing of primary colors of light to produce other colors?
a. refractive **b.** diffractive **c.** subtractive **d.** additive

For each of the statements below, write true *or rewrite the italicized part to make the statement true.*

9. ______________________ The clear-edged quality of the shadow that results when you put your hand into the path of light from a flashlight illustrates that light travels in a *curved* line.

10. ______________________ A primary pigment reflects *two* primary colors from white light.

11. ______________________ The spectrum of colors produced by an oil film on water is due to the *absorption of colors by a pigment.*

12. ______________________ The waves that cannot pass through a polarizing filter are those that are vibrating *parallel* to the polarizing axis.

Name ______________________

16 Chapter Assessment

Understanding Concepts Part B

Answer the following questions, showing your calculations.

1. What is the frequency of light with a wavelength of 7.00×10^{-7} m? What color is the light?

2. What is the illuminance, in lux, for a piece of paper on a table 3.0 m from a light source that is producing 1600 lm of luminous flux?

3. A lightbulb is 4.1 m from a surface. How much luminous flux must the bulb produce if the illuminance required is 22 lx?

4. What is the luminous intensity, in candelas, of a bulb with 2.00×10^3 lm of luminous flux?

5. A sodium vapor lamp emits light waves with wavelengths of 570 nm. What is the frequency of the waves?

6. What is the wavelength of light that has a frequency of 5.1×10^{14} Hz?

Name ______________________

16 Chapter Assessment

Applying Concepts

Answer the following questions, using complete sentences.

1. Define a ray and describe how rays are used to study light. What aspect of the nature of light does the ray model ignore?

2. Contrast luminous flux, luminous intensity, and illuminance.

3. Describe the relationship between illumination on a surface and the distance the surface is from the light source.

4. Explain why a dandelion appears yellow in white light. Is the process additive or subtractive?

5. How is a dye different from a pigment? How are the two similar?

6. How can you tell whether light is polarized?

Name ______________________

16 Chapter Assessment

Answer the following questions, showing your calculations.

7. The radius of Saturn's orbit is 1.43×10^9 km. How many minutes will it take light to cross its orbit?

8. One watt of electromagnetic energy produces about 500 lm of luminous flux. What is the illumination produced on a book by a fluorescent bulb that is 2.0 m from the book and that uses 40 W of electrical power? Assume that the bulb operates at 20 percent efficiency. In other words, only 0.2 of each watt of electric power provided to the bulb is converted to watts of usable electromagnetic energy in the form of light. (Hint: First calculate luminous flux, then illuminance.)

9. Suppose the fluorescent bulb in problem 8 were replaced by a 40-W incandescent bulb at the same distance from the book. Calculate the book's illuminance produced by the incandescent bulb, which operates at only 3 percent efficiency.

Date ______________ Period ______________ Name ______________________

17 Chapter Assessment

Use with Chapter 17.

Reflection and Refraction

Understanding Concepts Part A

Write the letter of the choice that best completes the statement or answers the question.

______ **1.** From which surface would light rays undergo regular reflection?

a. white construction paper

b. a telescope mirror

c. a piece of black cloth

d. a concrete sidewalk

______ **2.** Refraction occurs when _____.

a. light travels through two media that have different optical densities.

b. light strikes the boundary of two media that have the same optical density.

c. the angle of incidence equals zero.

d. the angle of reflection equals zero.

______ **3.** When light rays travel from one medium into a less optically dense medium, _____.

a. the rays speed up

b. the angle of refraction is smaller than the angle of incidence

c. the refracted rays bend toward the normal

d. the angle of incidence equals the angle of refraction

______ **4.** The index of refraction of the transparent mineral beryl is approximately 1.6. Transparent quartz has an index of 1.54. Diamond has an index of 2.42. Based on these facts, which statement is true?

a. All three minerals disperse light to the same extent.

b. Quartz disperses light more than does beryl.

c. Beryl disperses light more than does quartz.

d. Both beryl and quartz disperse light more than does diamond.

For each of the statements below, write true *or rewrite the italicized part to make the statement true.*

5. ______________________ The angle of incidence is always *less than* the angle of reflection.

6. ______________________ The higher the index of refraction is, the *faster* is the speed of light in the substance.

7. ______________________ For most practical purposes, the index of refraction of the air can be considered equal to *1.00*.

8. ______________________ A vacuum has an index of refraction that is *larger* than that of any substance.

9. ______________________ In a glass prism, the index of refraction for red light is *larger* than that for violet light.

Name ______________________

17 Chapter Assessment

Understanding Concepts Part B

Answer the following questions, showing your calculations.

1. Suppose that light rays traveling through air reach quartz at an angle of 35°. The index of refraction of quartz is 1.54. At what angle do the light rays travel within the quartz?

2. A light ray enters a substance from air at an angle of 55°. The light is refracted inside the substance and travels at an angle of 35°. What is the index of refraction of the substance?

3. Diamond has an index of refraction of 2.42. If it is immersed in water, which has an index of 1.33, and light rays in the water enter the diamond at a 53° angle, what is the angle of refraction inside the diamond?

4. The index of refraction of halite, or rock salt, is 1.54. What is the speed of light in that mineral?

Name ______________________

17 Chapter Assessment

Applying Concepts

Answer the following questions, using complete sentences.

1. Explain the difference between regular and diffuse reflection.

____

____

____

2. Explain the relationship between the sine of the angle of incidence and the sine of the angle of refraction of light rays traveling from a vacuum into a medium.

____

____

3. Mathematically express the relationship between indices of refraction for a light ray traveling from one medium into another.

____

4. What is total internal reflection and the critical angle?

____

____

____

____

____

5. How does the angle of refraction compare to the angle of incidence as a light ray passes from one medium into another with a lower index of refraction? What happens as the angle of incidence is increased?

____

____

____

6. Why is the sun still visible over the horizon for a time after the actual sunset?

____

____

____

____

Name ______________________

17 Chapter Assessment

Answer the following questions, showing your calculations.

7. Flint glass has indices of refraction of 1.57 for red light and 1.59 for violet light. If an incident ray of white light moving through the air reaches the glass at an angle of 65.0°, what will the angles of refraction be for the red and the violet light components?

8. Suppose that the flint glass from problem 7 is again used to refract white light. The source of the light is adjusted so that the light reaches the glass at an angle of 60.0°. What are the angles of refraction for the two colors of light?

9. A light ray in a tub of water makes an angle of incidence of 52° as it reaches the surface from below. The index of refraction of air is 1.00 and that of water is 1.33.

a. Show that the ray undergoes total internal reflection.

b. What is the value of the angle of reflection for the reflected ray?

____

Date ______________ Period ______________ Name ______________________

18 Chapter Assessment

Use with Chapter 18.

Mirrors and Lenses

Understanding Concepts Part A

Write the letter of the choice that best completes the statement or answers the question.

_____ **1.** The focal length of a spherical mirror equals _____.
- **a.** the radius of curvature
- **b.** twice the radius of curvature
- **c.** half the radius of curvature
- **d.** half the length of the principal axis

_____ **2.** When a real image is formed, _____.
- **a.** light rays seem to diverge behind the mirror
- **b.** light rays converge at the image
- **c.** the image cannot be projected on a screen
- **d.** the image is always inverted

_____ **3.** If an object is between a concave mirror and its focal point, the image will be _____.
- **a.** real and smaller than the object
- **b.** real and larger than the object
- **c.** virtual and smaller than the object
- **d.** virtual and larger than the object

_____ **4.** The image formed of an object located more than twice the focal length from a convex lens is _____.
- **a.** real and smaller than the object
- **b.** real and larger than the object
- **c.** virtual and smaller than the object
- **d.** virtual and larger than the object

For each of the statements below, write true *or rewrite the italicized part to make the statement true.*

5. ______________________ *Chromatic* aberration can be reduced by joining together a converging lens and a diverging lens.

6. ______________________ Concave lenses have *positive* focal lengths.

7. ______________________ Parabolic mirrors are often used in *microscopes*.

8. ______________________ Rays parallel to the principal axis of a *concave* mirror converge at the focal point.

9. ______________________ *Magnification* is equal to the size of the image divided by the size of the object.

Name ______________________________

18 Chapter Assessment

Understanding Concepts Part B

1. A thimble is 32.0 cm from a concave mirror. The focal point of the mirror is 11.0 cm. Where is the image located?

2. What are the size and orientation of the image of the thimble from problem 1 if the thimble itself is 2.50 cm tall?

3. What is the magnification in problem 2?

4. A child who is 1.1 m tall is standing 6.0 m from a concave mirror. The child's image is 0.40 m behind the mirror. What is the size of the image?

Name ______________________

18 Chapter Assessment

5. What is the focal length of the mirror in problem 4?

6. An object is 5.00 cm from a convex lens that has a focal length of 6.00 cm. Locate the image and determine whether it is real or virtual.

7. What is the focal length of a concave lens that forms an image with a d_i value of –10.0 cm when an object is 35.0 cm from the lens?

Name ______________________

18 Chapter Assessment

Applying Concepts

Answer the following questions, using complete sentences.

1. What happens to a light ray that enters parallel to the principal axis of a concave mirror? What happens to a ray that passes through the focal point of such a mirror before being reflected?

2. Explain what causes spherical aberration.

3. Contrast convex and concave lenses.

4. Contrast the image formed by a converging lens when an object is located more than twice the focal length from the lens, with the image formed when the object is between the lens and the focus.

5. Contrast concave and convex mirrors.

6. Explain the operation of mirrors used in stores to observe shoppers.

Name ______________________

18 Chapter Assessment

Answer the following questions, showing your calculations.

7. You want to create a 0.035-m image of a flower that is 1.00 m high and 10.0 m from a concave mirror. What must the radius of curvature of the mirror be?

8. If a vehicle 2.0 m high is 4.6 m from a car's convex mirror, find the position and size of the image, given that the radius of curvature is 0.80 m. Is the image real or virtual? Is it erect or inverted? Give reasons for your answer.

Name ______________________________

18 Chapter Assessment

9. A object that is 0.95 cm tall and 4.2 cm from a convex lens produces a real image that is 2.8 cm from the other side of the lens.

   a. What is the size of the image? Is the image erect or inverted? Is the image enlarged or reduced?

   b. What is the magnification of the lens? What is the focal length of the lens?

Date ______________ Period ______________ Name ______________________

19 Chapter Assessment

Use with Chapter 19.

Diffraction and Interference of Light

Understanding Concepts Part A

Write the letter of the choice that best completes the statement or answers the question.

_____ **1.** The destructive and constructive interference of light that passes through two closely spaced slits produces _____.
- **a.** a single continuous spectrum
- **b.** interference fringes
- **c.** a continuous white band
- **d.** a single band of one color

_____ **2.** The bending of waves around the edges of barriers is called _____.
- **a.** diffraction
- **b.** refraction
- **c.** reflection
- **d.** dispersion

_____ **3.** The paths of light waves that come from two slits and that interfere to form first-order lines _____.
- **a.** are exactly the same length
- **b.** differ in length by the wavelength of the light
- **c.** are parallel
- **d.** are perpendicular

_____ **4.** When light passes through a single slit, which of the following appears?
- **a.** a series of equally bright bands
- **b.** a dark central band, with bright bands to the sides
- **c.** a bright central band, with dimmer bands to the sides
- **d.** a single wide bright band

_____ **5.** A pair of closely spaced stars can be seen as a single star because a telescope lens has limited _____.
- **a.** index of refraction
- **b.** chromatic aberration
- **c.** reflective ability
- **d.** resolving power

_____ **6.** The effects of diffraction on the ability of telescopes to distinguish between closely spaced stars can be reduced by _____.
- **a.** increasing the size of the lens
- **b.** decreasing the size of the lens
- **c.** using red filters
- **d.** reducing the amount of light entering the telescope

For each of the statements below, write true *or* rewrite *the italicized part to make the statement true.*

7. ______________________ Diffraction is *more obvious* for sound waves than for light waves.

8. ______________________ For a *single-slit* experiment, the distance x is equal to $\lambda L/w$.

9. ______________________ The symbol used to represent the distance between two slits is *L*.

10. ______________________ For a two-slit experiment, the wavelength equals $\lambda d/L$.

Name ____________

19 Chapter Assessment

Understanding Concepts Part B

Answer the following questions, showing your calculations.

1. Suppose the separation between two slits is 1.72×10^{-5} m and the screen is 0.650 m from the slits. If monochromatic violet light with a wavelength of 4.50×10^{-7} m passes through the slits, how far from the central band will the first band of the violet light appear?

2. A red laser beam falls on two slits that are 1.95×10^{-5} m apart. A first-order line appears 4.42×10^{-2} m from the central bright line. If the screen is 1.25 m from the slits, what is the wavelength of the light?

3. Suppose that monochromatic light that has a wavelength of 570 nm passes through two slits that are separated by 1.90×10^{-5} m and that are 0.800 m from the screen. What is the distance from the central line to the first-order line?

Name ______________________

19 Chapter Assessment

4. Suppose that the double slit in problem 3 is replaced by a single slit 0.0900 mm wide. What is the distance from the center of the central band to the first dark band?

5. Suppose that a diffraction grating has 6.00×10^3 lines per centimeter. The screen is 0.400 m from the grating. If monochromatic light shines on the grating, and the first-order line appears on the screen 12.9 cm from the central line, what is the wavelength of the light?

Name ______________________

19 Chapter Assessment

Applying Concepts

Answer the following questions, using complete sentences

1. Why are the edges of shadows not perfectly sharp? What is this phenomenon called?

2. Why did diffraction suggest that the corpuscular model of light is not entirely correct? What experiment first measured wavelengths of light?

3. Explain how single-slit diffraction causes dark bands.

4. Compare the diffraction of light and sound, and account for any differences.

5. Contrast the interference patterns formed by double slits with those formed by diffraction gratings.

6. Can the values for the wavelengths of the components of white light be measured directly with a grating spectrometer? Give a reason for your answer.

Name ______________________

19 Chapter Assessment

Answer the following questions, showing your calculations.

7. The range of wavelengths for visible light is about 400–700 nm. At what angle will the first-order line for violet light of wavelength 400 nm be produced by a diffraction grating that has 1.00×10^4 lines per centimeter?

8. At what angle will the first-order line for red light of wavelength 700 nm be produced by the diffraction grating in problem 7?

9. When white light shines on it, a diffraction grating forms a number of spectra on either side of the central band. The spectra can be assigned a number corresponding to their order. The symbol for this order number is m ($m = 1$ for first order, etc.). The equation $\sin \theta = m\lambda/d$ gives the angle for light that appears in a spectral band of order m. Apply this equation to find the angle for the third-order violet light that has a wavelength of 400 nm. The lines on the diffraction grating are 1.00×10^{-5} m apart.

Name ______________________

19 Chapter Assessment

10. Using the same procedure as in problem 9, find the angle for the second-order red light that has a wavelength of 700 nm, using the same grating. Compare the angle to the one calculated in problem 9. What can you conclude about these second- and third-order spectral bands, in terms of overlap?

11. Rearrange the equation $\sin\theta = m\lambda/d$ to find the upper limit for observable wavelength that can be observed in the fourth order for a diffraction grating that has 5.00×10^3 lines per centimeter. Note that the angle for the longest observable wavelength cannot exceed 90°.

Date ______________ Period ______________ Name ______________________

20 Chapter Assessment

Use with Chapter 20.

Static Electricity

Understanding Concepts Part A

For each of the statements below, write true *or rewrite the italicized part to make the statement true.*

1. ______________________ Bits of paper stick to a plastic comb that has been rubbed because of *electric charge.*

2. ______________________ When electrons are transferred from one object to another, positive and negative charges are *separated.*

3. ______________________ Charges in *conductors* cannot easily move around.

4. ______________________ Coulomb's law *can* be used to find magnitude and the direction of an electric force between two charged objects.

5. ______________________ Touching an electroscope with a negatively charged rod is an example of charging by *induction.*

Write the letter of the choice that best completes the statement or answers the question.

______ **6.** When an electroscope is charged, its leaves spread apart because _____.

a. unlike charges repel

b. charges exert force on other charges over a distance

c. positive charges spread over the metal surfaces

d. negative charges spread over the metal surfaces

______ **7.** The force that charge q_A exerts on charge q_B is opposite and _____ the force that charge q_B exerts on q_A.

a. greater than **b.** less than **c.** equal to

______ **8.** Electric force is a vector quantity because it has magnitude and _____.

a. direction **b.** duration **c.** frequency **d.** strength

______ **9.** If an electroscope that is negatively charged is touched with a rod with a negative charge, _____.

a. there will be no effect

b. the leaves will spread farther apart

c. the leaves will fall

d. the electroscope will become positively charged

Name ______________________________

20 Chapter Assessment

Understanding Concepts Part B

Answer the following questions, showing your calculations.

1. Assuming the force exerted between two spheres is 64 N, what will be the magnitude of the force if the distance is doubled? Tripled?

2. A positive charge of 3.6×10^{-5} C and a negative charge of -2.4×10^{-5} C are 0.034 m apart. What is the force between the two particles?

3. The force between two objects is 64 N. One object has a positive charge of 1.4×10^{-6} C, while the other has a negative charge of 1.8×10^{-6} C. How far apart are the two objects?

Name ______________________________

20 Chapter Assessment

4. Two negative charges of 4.2×10^{-8} C are separated by 0.46 m. What is the magnitude of the force acting on each object?

5. Two objects exert a force of 4.2 N on each other. The distance between the objects is 0.36 m. The charge on one object is 2.8×10^{-9} C. What is the charge on the second object?

Name ______________________________

20 Chapter Assessment

Applying Concepts

Answer the following questions, using complete sentences.

1. Which of the following would you use to prevent the spread of an electric charge: copper, plastic, or graphite? Explain your answer.

____

____

____

____

2. Explain how objects can become charged when individual charges cannot be created or destroyed.

____

____

3. Why do socks and other pieces of clothing stick together after being tumbled in a dryer?

____

____

____

____

4. Distinguish between charging by conduction and charging by induction.

____

____

____

____

5. Does charging by induction or conduction occur during a thunderstorm? Explain.

____

____

____

____

6. Two positive charges are located 2 cm apart. Charge q_A is 2×10^{-9} C and charge q_B is 3×10^{-9} C. Is the force between these charges attractive or repulsive? Explain your answer.

____

____

20 Chapter Assessment

Answer the following questions, showing your calculations.

7. Two objects, one having twice the charge of the other, are separated by 0.78 m and exert a force of 3.8×10^3 N. What is the magnitude of charge on each object?

8. The drawing below shows the charges on three objects and the distances between them. Charges A and C are 90° apart with respect to charge B. Calculate the magnitude of the net charge acting on charge B.

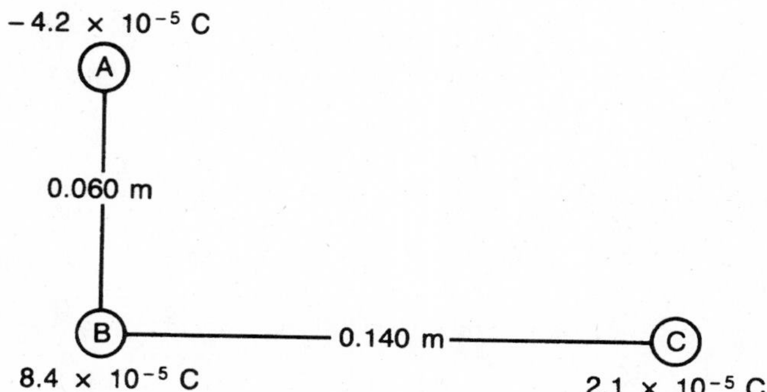

Name ______________________

20 Chapter Assessment

9. Draw a diagram of the force vectors of A on B and C on B. What is the vector angle of the net force acting on charge B? Add this vector to your drawing, showing its approximate position.

Date ______________ Period ______________ Name ________________________

21 Chapter Assessment

Use with Chapter 21.

Electric Fields

Understanding Concepts Part A

Write the letter of the choice that best completes each statement.

_____ **1.** An electric field is equal to _____.

a. force per unit mass
b. force per unit charge
c. force per unit time
d. force times direction

_____ **2.** The force on a test charge in an electric field is _____.

a. directly proportional to the magnitude of the field
b. inversely proportional to the magnitude of the field
c. inversely proportional to the square of the magnitude of the field
d. unrelated to the magnitude of the field

_____ **3.** The strength of the force on a charge in an electric field depends on _____.

a. the direction of the field
b. the magnitude of the field
c. the size of the charge
d. both the magnitude of the field and the size of the charge

_____ **4.** As an electric field becomes stronger, the field lines should be drawn _____.

a. thicker
b. thinner
c. closer together
d. farther apart

_____ **5.** A good device to indicate electric field lines is _____.

a. a Leyden jar
b. a capacitor
c. a lightning rod
d. a Van de Graaff machine

For each of the statements below, write true *or rewrite the italicized part to make the statement true.*

6. ______________________ With two *like* charges, you must do work to pull one charge away from the other.

7. ______________________ In a *uniform electric field,* the potential difference between two points is found using the equation $\Delta V = Ed$.

8. ______________________ Robert Millikan determined that the charge of a *proton* is 1.6×10^{-19} C.

9. ______________________ Touching an object to Earth to eliminate excess charge is *grounding.*

10. ______________________ The charges on a hollow conductor are found on the *inner* surface.

11. ______________________ A *capacitor* is made up of two conductors separated by an insulator.

Name ______________________________

21 Chapter Assessment

Understanding Concepts Part B

1. A force of 0.43 N acts on a positive charge of 2.4×10^{-6} C at a certain distance. What is the electric field intensity at that distance?

2. What charge does a test charge have when a force of 3.60×10^{-6} N acts on it at a point where the electric field intensity is 1.60×10^{-5} N/C?

3. The electric field intensity between two charged plates is 2.80×10^{4} N/C. The plates are 0.0640 m apart. What is the potential difference between the plates in volts?

4. A voltmeter connected between two plates registers 38.2 V. The plates are separated by a distance of 0.046 m. What is the field intensity between the plates?

5. How much work is done to transfer 0.47 C of charge through a potential difference of 12 V?

6. A 9.0-V battery does 1.0×10^{3} J of work transferring charge. How much charge is transferred?

Name ______________________

21 Chapter Assessment

Applying Concepts

Answer the following questions, using complete sentences.

1. Compare an electric field to a gravitational field.

____

____

____

____

____

____

2. What is the direction of an electric field between a negative and a positive charge?

____

____

3. Explain why electric potential energy is larger when two like charges are close together than when two unlike charges are close together.

____

____

____

____

____

4. If a high-voltage wire falls on a car, will the people inside be safe from electrocution? Explain your answer.

____

____

____

____

5. What is the net charge on a capacitor? Explain your answer.

____

____

____

Name ______________________

21 Chapter Assessment

Answer the following questions, showing your calculations.

6. A force of 7.60×10^3 N acts on a charge of 1.60×10^{-2} C in a uniform field over a distance of 0.0440 m. What is the potential difference of this system?

7. How much work is done by a system in which the force is 6.8×10^4 N, the potential difference is 4.2 V, and the electric field intensity is 1.2×10^{-3} N/C?

8. How much energy is stored in a capacitor of 12.2 μF that has been charged to 4.26×10^2 V?

9. How much power is required to charge a capacitor of 9.4 μF to 5.4×10^2 V in 48 s?

Date ______________ Period ______________ Name ______________________

22 Chapter Assessment

Use with Chapter 22.

Current Electricity

Understanding Concepts Part A

Use each of the following terms once to complete the statements below.

ampere	electric current	potential difference	resistance
electric circuit	kinetic energy	power	

1. ______________ A charge pump creates a flow of charged particles, or _____.
2. ______________ A closed loop through which charges can flow is a(n) _____.
3. ______________ When a water wheel drives a generator, the generator converts the _____ of the water to electric energy.
4. ______________ The rate at which energy is transferred is _____.
5. ______________ The unit used to measure the rate of flow of electric current is a(n) _____.
6. ______________ The _____ of a conductor can be determined if potential difference and current are known.
7. ______________ A device that has constant resistance and appears to be independent of the _____ is said to obey Ohm's law.

Write the letter of the choice that best completes each statement.

_____ **8.** The current flowing in an electric circuit can be increased by _____.

a. increasing voltage or decreasing resistance

b. decreasing voltage or increasing resistance

c. increasing voltage and increasing resistance

d. decreasing voltage and decreasing resistance

_____ **9.** A device that measures the amount of current in a circuit is a(n) _____.

a. potentiometer **b.** resistor **c.** voltmeter **d.** ammeter

_____ **10.** Space heaters convert most of the electric energy in a circuit into _____ energy.

a. light **b.** thermal **c.** mechanical **d.** sound

_____ **11.** Electricity is carried long distances at high voltages because _____.

a. this reduces the current and less power is lost as thermal energy

b. this reduces the resistance and less power is lost as thermal energy

c. current cannot be changed to reduce thermal energy

d. capacitance cannot be changed to reduce thermal energy.

_____ **12.** Utility companies measure energy used in _____.

a. joules **b.** kilowatt-hours **c.** watt-seconds **d.** watts

Name ______________________

22 Chapter Assessment

Understanding Concepts Part B

Answer each of the following questions, showing your calculations.

1. A portable compact-disk player receives its energy from a 9.0-V cell. The current used to operate the player is 135 A.

a. How many joules of energy does the cell deliver to the CD player each second?

b. How much power in watts does the CD player use?

c. How much energy does the CD player use to play a selection 3.0 min long?

2. What voltage is applied to a 6.80-Ω resistor if the current is 3.20 A?

3. An electric buzzer is connected across a 4.2-V difference in potential. The current through the buzzer is 1.8 A.

a. What is the power rating of the buzzer?

b. How much electric energy does the buzzer convert in 1.5 min?

4. An electric blanket with a resistance of 8.6 Ω is connected to a 120-V source.

a. What is the current in the circuit?

b. How much heat is produced if the blanket is turned on for 15 min?

Name ______________________

22 Chapter Assessment

Applying Concepts

Answer the following sentences, using complete sentences.

1. What is the difference between an ampere and a volt?

____

____

____

____

2. Identify the parts of this schematic. Will current flow through the circuit? Give a reason for your answer.

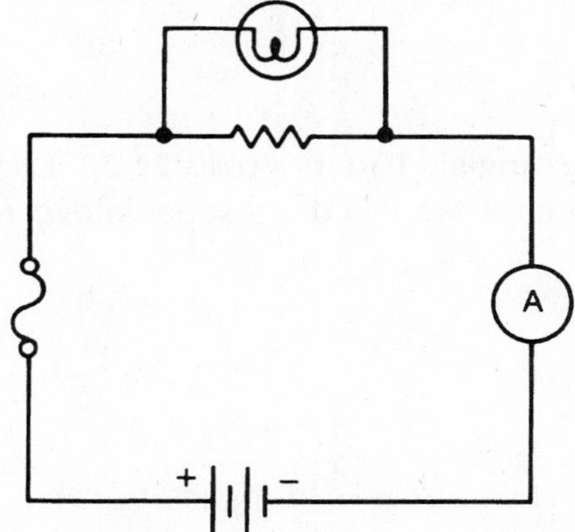

____

3. Could a voltmeter be substituted for the ammeter shown in the schematic in problem 2? Give a reason for your answer.

____

____

4. What would happen to current if voltage and resistance were doubled?

____

____

5. Which has a greater effect on the amount of thermal energy produced in a heater, the current or the resistance of the heater? Give a reason for your answer.

____

____

____

Name ______________________

22 Chapter Assessment

Answer the following questions, showing your calculations.

6. An electric motor operates an elevator the mass of which is 2.0×10^3 kg. The elevator rises 120 m in 32 s. The motor has a resistance while operating of 34.0 Ω and is connected across a 2.4×10^3-V source. What percentage of electric energy is converted to kinetic energy?

7. A three-pack of 1.5-V hearing-aid batteries costs $4.26. Each battery puts out 8.0 mA of current. Each battery lasts for 15 days. What is the cost per kilowatt hour to operate the hearing aid with one battery?

8. While waiting for the school bus, you keep your hands warm in a pair of electric gloves. The heating element in each glove has a resistance of 8.0 Ω. Each glove operates from a 12-V source. The thermal energy produced by each glove is 640 J. You wait for the bus for 3.0 min. When the bus arrives, are the electric gloves still producing heat?

9. A model electric train makes one complete pass around a circular track every 15 s. The train's motor has a resistance of 6.0 Ω and is connected to a 70.0-V source. How much energy will the train use in 12 complete passes around the track?

Date ______________ Period ______________ Name ______________________

23 Chapter Assessment

Use with Chapter 23.

Series and Parallel Circuits

Understanding Concepts Part A

Write the letter of the choice that best completes the statement or answers the question.

_____ **1.** If four electric devices are connected in a series circuit, then the number of current paths is equal to _____.

a. one **b.** two **c.** three **d.** four

_____ **2.** A series circuit contains a generator, an ammeter, and a lamp. The current in the lamp is _____.

a. equal to the current in the ammeter, but greater than the current in the generator

b. less than the current in the ammeter

c. equal to the current in the generator and equal to the current in the ammeter

d. less than the current in the generator

_____ **3.** A series circuit contains four resistors. What is the equivalent resistance of the circuit?

a. $4R$

b. $R_1 + R_2 + R_3 + R_4$

c. $R/4$

d. $(R_1 + R_2 + R_3 + R_4)/4$

_____ **4.** A series circuit has a 120-V generator but requires a 60-V potential source. To achieve the desired potential, a _____ can be used.

a. photoresistor

b. sensor

c. voltage divider

d. semiconductor

_____ **5.** If three resistors are connected in parallel, there are _____ current paths in the circuit.

a. one **b.** two **c.** three **d.** four

_____ **6.** In an electric circuit, _____ are switches that act as safety devices.

a. fuses and circuit breakers

b. fuses and voltage dividers

c. ammeters

d. combined circuits

For each of the statements below, write true *or* false.

7. ____________________ To measure the current through a resistor, an ammeter should be connected in series with the resistor.

8. ____________________ The equivalent resistance of a parallel circuit is always less than the resistance of any resistor in the circuit.

9. ____________________ A voltmeter should have a very low resistance so that it causes the largest possible changes in currents and voltages in the circuit.

10. ____________________ The resistance of an ammeter should be as low as possible.

11. ____________________ To measure the current across a resistor, connect a voltmeter in parallel with the resistor.

Name ______________________

23 Chapter Assessment

Understanding Concepts Part B

Answer the following questions, showing your calculations.

1. Two resistors of 3.0 Ω and 8.0 Ω are connected in series across a 9.0-V battery.

a. What is the equivalent resistance of the circuit?

b. What is the current through the 3.0-Ω resistor?

c. What is the current through the 8.0-Ω resistor?

d. What is the voltage drop across each resistor?

2. A 15.0-Ω bell and an 8.0-Ω lamp are connected in parallel and placed across a difference in potential of 42 V.

a. What is the equivalent resistance of the circuit?

b. What is the current in the circuit?

c. What is the current through each resistor?

d. What is the voltage drop across each resistor?

Name ______________________

23 Chapter Assessment

Applying Concepts

Answer the following questions, using complete sentences.

1. A string of holiday lights has 15 bulbs connected in series. If one of the bulbs burns out, what happens to the other bulbs? Give a reason for your answer.

____

____

2. What happens to resistance when a resistor is added in parallel to a circuit that already has two resistors?

____

____

3. How is it possible to use more than one electric appliance at a time in a house?

____

____

4. A circuit has five identical resistors, A, B, C, D, and E. Resistors A, D, and E have the same potential difference across them. What kind of circuit is this? Give a reason for your answer.

____

____

5. What would happen to the current in a circuit if a voltmeter were substituted for an ammeter?

____

____

____

6. Explain why a ground-fault interrupter is often required by law in electric outlets in bathrooms and kitchens, but not in other rooms in a house.

____

____

____

____

7. Why does turning on additional appliances on the same circuit breaker increase the current through the wires?

____

____

____

Name ______________________

23 Chapter Assessment

Answer the following questions, showing your calculations.

8. Find the reading of each ammeter and each voltmeter in the diagram below.

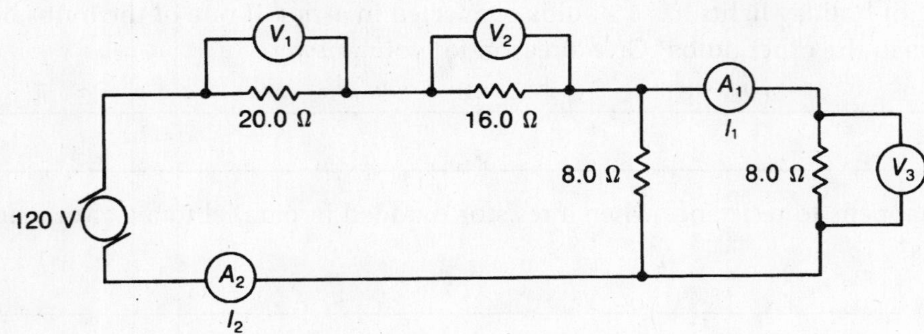

The equivalent resistance of the resistors in parallel is

For the entire circuit, the equivalent resistance is

The voltage drop across each 8.0-Ω resistor is

9. What is the power in watts used by each resistance in the diagram above?

Date ______________ Period ______________ Name ______________________

24 Chapter Assessment

Use with Chapter 24.

Magnetic Fields

Understanding Concepts Part A

Write the letter of the choice that best completes each statement.

_____ **1.** An object that is magnetic has _____.

a. only a south-seeking pole

b. only an east-seeking pole

c. an east-seeking pole and a west-seeking pole

d. a north-seeking pole and a south-seeking pole

_____ **2.** The magnitude of the current in a wire is _____ to the magnetic field around the wire.

a. proportional **c.** equal

b. inversely proportional **d.** parallel

_____ **3.** Increasing the number of loops in an electromagnet causes the strength of the magnetic field to _____.

a. increase **b.** decrease **c.** remain the same **d.** double

_____ **4.** In a magnetic material, the _____ act like tiny electromagnets.

a. atoms **b.** electrons **c.** protons **d.** neutrons

_____ **5.** The magnetic force on a current-carrying wire in a magnetic field is _____ the direction of the current.

a. opposite to **b.** parallel to **c.** perpendicular to **d.** the same as

For each of the statements below, write true *or rewrite the italicized portion to make the statement true.*

6. ____________________ The *magnitude* of the magnetic force on a current-carrying wire depends on the strength of the magnetic field, the current in the wire, and the length of wire in the magnetic field.

7. ____________________ When two parallel wires carry currents in opposite directions, their magnetic fields *attract* each other.

8. ____________________ A device used to measure very small electric currents is *an ammeter.*

9. ____________________ In an electric motor, current is reversed every *complete turn.*

10. ____________________ The speed of an electric motor can be controlled by *varying* the current flow.

Name ______________________________

24 Chapter Assessment

Understanding Concepts Part B

Answer the following questions, showing your calculations.

1. A wire carries a current of 6.0 A. The wire is at right angles to a uniform magnetic field, and 0.80 m of the wire is in the field. The force on the wire is 0.62 N. What is the strength of the magnetic field?

2. A wire is at right angles to a uniform magnetic field with magnetic induction of 0.400 T. The current through the wire is 4.00 A. What is the force that acts on the wire when 60.0 cm is in the field?

3. A wire carries a current of 12 A. The wire is at right angles to a uniform magnetic field that exerts a force of 0.50 N on the wire when 2.0 m of the wire is in the field. What is the induction of the magnetic field?

4. A wire is at right angles to a magnetic field that exerts a force of 2.4 N on the wire. A current of 8.6 A flows through the wire. The induction of the magnetic field is 0.66 T. What length of wire is in the field?

5. A high-speed electron travels at right angles to a magnetic field that has an induction of 0.420 T. The electron is traveling at 3.46×10^7 m/s. What is the force acting on the electron?

Name ______________________

24 Chapter Assessment

Applying Concepts

Answer the following questions, using complete sentences.

1. If all electrons create magnetic fields, why aren't all materials magnets?

2. How are the forces between charges similar to the forces between magnetic poles?

3. Suppose you have two bar magnets. Only one of the magnets has north and south poles labeled. How would you determine which are the south and north poles on the unlabeled magnet?

4. An electrical wire carries current in a straight line from east to west. What is the direction of the resulting magnetic field above the wire? What is the direction of the field below the wire?

5. If an electromagnet is used to pick up nails and other metal objects, what happens when the current is turned off?

6. If a permanent magnet is dropped or struck by a hammer, it may lose its magnetism. Explain why.

Name ______________________

24 Chapter Assessment

Answer the following questions, showing your calculations.

7. A section of wire and resistors in a circuit has a total resistance of 6.0 Ω and a potential difference of 120 V. If 0.40 M of the wire is placed in a uniform magnetic field at right angles to the field, the force on the wire is 0.50 N. What is the strength of the magnetic field?

8. A proton travels at 1.0×10^5 m/s perpendicular to a uniform magnetic field of 5.5×10^{-5} T. What is the magnitude of the acceleration of the proton?

Date ______________ Period ______________ Name ______________________

25 Chapter Assessment

Use with Chapter 25.

Electromagnetic Induction

Understanding Concepts Part A

For each of the statements below, write true *or rewrite the italicized part to make the statement true.*

1. An electric current is generated in a wire when the wire is moved so that it *cuts across* magnetic field lines.

____

2. Current can be made to flow in a stationary wire by moving a magnetic field *parallel* to the wire.

____

3. The electromotive force depends only on magnetic field strength, the length of the wire in the magnetic field, and the *velocity* of the wire in the magnetic field.

____

4. An electric generator converts mechanical energy to *thermal* energy.

____

5. An electric motor is almost identical in construction to an electric generator, but the motor converts electric energy to *mechanical* energy.

____

6. According to Lenz's law, the direction of induced current is such that the magnetic field resulting from the induced current *strengthens* the change in field that caused the current.

____

7. If a generator produces only a small current, then the opposing force on the armature will be small and the armature will be *hard* to turn.

____

8. When a motor is first turned on, a *large* current flows because of the low resistance of the motor.

____

9. If the N-pole of a magnet is moved toward the right end of a coil of wire, the right end of the coil becomes an N-pole and *attracts* the magnet.

____

10. When a piece of metal is moved through a magnetic field, *eddy currents* are generated in the metal.

____

11. In a *step-up* transformer, the primary voltage is greater than the secondary voltage.

____

Name ______________________

25 Chapter Assessment

Understanding Concepts Part B

Answer the following questions, showing your calculations.

1. A wire 42.0 m long moves directly upward through a magnetic field of 6.20×10^{-4} T at a speed of 18.0 m/s. What *EMF* is induced in the wire?

2. An AC generator develops a maximum *EMF* of 620 V. What effective *EMF* does the generator deliver to an external circuit?

3. A step-up transformer has 125 turns on its primary coil. Its secondary coil consists of 1440 turns. The primary coil receives an AC current at 120 V.

a. What is the voltage across the secondary circuit?

b. The current in the secondary coil is 3.6 A. What current flows in the primary circuit?

c. What is the power input and output of the transformer?

4. The primary coil of a transformer has 640 turns and is connected to a 240-V source. How many turns would be needed in the secondary coil to supply 800 V?

Name ______________________

25 Chapter Assessment

Applying Concepts

Answer the following questions, using complete sentences.

1. A loop of wire is connected to a galvanometer. If a bar magnet is dropped through the loop, what happens to the galvanometer?

2. A bar magnet and a loop of wire are moving parallel to each other at the same velocity. What is the voltage induced in the loop? Give a reason for your answer.

3. What happens to induced *EMF* when magnetic field strength is doubled?

4. Compare the operation of an electric motor with that of an electric generator.

5. Why do the lights in a room dim momentarily when a large appliance is turned on?

6. What happens to the primary voltage when the number of turns on a secondary transformer coil is doubled?

Name ______________________

25 Chapter Assessment

Answer the following questions, showing your calculations.

7. The current flowing through a wire is 2.4×10^{-3} A. The wire is connected across a circuit of 8.0-Ω resistance. If 0.60 m of the wire is moving perpendicularly through the magnetic field of 0.48 T, what is the velocity of the wire?

8. A space vehicle is sent to Jupiter to explore the planet's properties from orbit. The vehicle travels 1.0×10^3 km/min. When in orbit, the probe deploys a horizontal antenna that is 120 m long. Data received on Earth indicate that the probe is flying over a location where the magnetic field is 0.18 T. What voltage is induced between the antenna's tips?

9. An alternating-current generator requires 120 J of mechanical energy per second to produce 100 W of effective power.

a. What is the efficiency of the generator?

b. If the total resistance of turns in the wire in the generator is 12 Ω, what is the maximum current produced?

Date ______________ Period ______________ Name ______________________

26 Chapter Assessment

Use with Chapter 26.

Electromagnetism

Understanding Concepts Part A

Write the letter of the choice that best completes each statement.

_____ **1.** In a cathode-ray tube, an electric field pulls electrons out of the _____ toward the _____.
- **a.** negatively charged cathode, positively charged anode
- **b.** positively charged anode, negatively charged cathode
- **c.** negatively charged anode, positively charged cathode
- **d.** positively charged cathode, negatively charged anode

_____ **2.** The masses of positive ions can be measured precisely using a _____.
- **a.** Thomson tube
- **b.** Bainbridge tube
- **c.** cathode-ray tube
- **d.** mass spectrometer

_____ **3.** In an electromagnetic wave, the electric and magnetic fields are _____ to each other and _____ to the direction of wave motion.
- **a.** at right angles, perpendicular
- **b.** at right angles, parallel
- **c.** parallel, at right angles
- **d.** opposite, parallel

_____ **4.** To produce an electromagnetic wave, an antenna can be connected to _____.
- **a.** a battery
- **b.** an alternating current source
- **c.** a direct current source
- **d.** a magnet

_____ **5.** An electromagnetic wave produced by an antenna is _____.
- **a.** perpendicular to the direction of the antenna wires
- **b.** independent of the direction of the antenna wires
- **c.** parallel to the direction of the antenna wires
- **d.** dependent on the direction of the current

For each of the statements below, write true *or* false.

6. ______________ An electromagnetic wave can be produced only by an antenna connected to an alternating current source.

7. ______________ Quartz crystals have a property called piezoelectricity that can generate electromagnetic waves.

8. ______________ The *EMF* across the terminals of a reception antenna is largest if the length of the antenna is one-half the wavelength of the wave.

9. ______________ Waves carry energy as well as information.

10. ______________ X rays are in the same range of wavelengths as visible light.

Name ______________________________

26 Chapter Assessment

Understanding Concepts Part B

Answer the following questions, showing your calculations.

1. An object passes through a magnetic field of 6.2×10^{-2} T. The object's speed is 8.4×10^{3} m/s. What is the electric field intensity?

2. An unknown particle having a mass of 2.4×20^{-27} kg and a charge of 3.2×10^{-19} C passes through a magnetic field of 5.6×10^{-1} T. The velocity of the particle is 6.8×10^{3} m/s. What is the radius of its path?

3. A particle with a mass of 4.1×10^{-27} kg and a charge of 6.4×10^{-19} C crosses a magnetic field that measures 2.6×10^{-2} T. The particle assumes a circular path with a radius of 1.2×10^{-1} m. At what speed is the particle moving?

4. A particle passing through a magnetic field has a mass of 6.5×10^{-27} kg and is moving at 3.2×10^{4} m/s. The charge on the particle is 2.5×10^{-18} C and the radius of its circular path through the field is 4.1×10^{-2} m. What is the strength of the magnetic field?

5. A particle with a mass of 3.34×10^{-27} kg and a charge of 1.6×10^{-19} C passes through a magnetic field of 3.8×10^{-3} T. This causes the nucleus to assume a circular path with a radius of 0.060 m. A potential difference of what value accelerated the particle?

Name ______________________

26 Chapter Assessment

Applying Concepts

1. A scientist wants to know how much of a given pollutant is found in the air near a factory. Ordinarily, the pollutant is found in minute amounts. How might the scientist obtain this information?

2. What is piezoelectricity? How does it produce an electromagnetic field?

3. Explain what happens when you change the setting on your radio from one station to another.

4. If the orientation of the electric and magnetic fields generated by an electromagnetic wave is known, is it possible to determine the direction of the motion of the wave? Give a reason for your answer.

5. Briefly explain how an electromagnetic wave is produced by the antenna of a television broadcast station.

6. Why did Thomson use the charge-to-mass ratio to find the mass of an electron?

Name ______________________

26 Chapter Assessment

Answer the following questions, showing your calculations.

7. In an attempt to identify an unknown atom, a research team has narrowed the possibilities to a few atoms. The nuclear composition (protons and neutrons) of several atoms is shown in the table below. Each proton or neutron has a mass of 1.67×10^{-24} kg. Experiments have yielded the following data: The ion of the atom has a negative charge of 1.6×10^{-19} C. When passing through a magnetic field of 7.8×10^{-3} T at a speed of 7.9 m/s, the ion develops a circular path that has a radius of 8.3×10^{-4} m. What is the identity of the atom?

Atom	Protons	Neutrons
chlorine	17	18
argon	18	22
bromine	35	44
krypton	36	48
iodine	53	74

8. Radon, Rn, is a radioactive element. As such it releases certain particles. Assume you are a researcher attempting to identify the particle released. It has a charge of 3.2×10^{-19} C. When passing through a magnetic field of 2.0 T across a potential difference of 1.6×10^{7} V, the particle follows a circular path that has a radius of 4.1×10^{-1} m. What is the mass of the particle?

Date ______________ Period ______________ Name ______________________

27 Chapter Assessment

Use with Chapter 27.

Quantum Theory

Understanding Concepts Part A

Write the letter of the choice that best completes each statement.

_____ **1.** According to Planck's hypothesis, _____.
- **a.** the energy of an incandescent body is quantized
- **b.** the variable *n* can have any real number value
- **c.** the frequency of vibration is inversely proportional to the energy
- **d.** atoms constantly radiate electromagnetic waves when they vibrate

_____ **2.** If the incident light on a photocell is very dim, electrons will _____.
- **a.** never be ejected
- **b.** be ejected only after they have absorbed energy for a long time
- **c.** be ejected immediately if the frequency is at or above the threshold frequency
- **d.** be ejected after a long time if the frequency is below the threshold frequency

_____ **3.** The slope of a graph of the kinetic energy of ejected electrons versus the frequency of the incident radiation is equal to _____.
- **a.** Planck's constant
- **b.** the wavelength of the radiation
- **c.** the work function
- **d.** the threshold frequency

_____ **4.** Compton's X-ray experiment showed that _____.
- **a.** only photons behave like particles
- **b.** only electrons behave like particles
- **c.** momentum and kinetic energy are conserved when photons collide with electrons
- **d.** photons have more mass than electrons

For each of the statements below, write true *or rewrite the italicized part to make the statement true.*

5. ______________________ In a star's spectrum, the frequency of the radiation emitted increases as the star's temperature *decreases.*

6. ______________________ Einstein theorized that the momentum of a photon is *inversely* proportional to the wavelength.

7. ______________________ The wavelength of a particle is *inversely proportional* to the particle's momentum.

8. ______________________ Because of the Compton effect, when light of short wavelengths is used to measure the location of a particle, the particle's *position* is changed.

9. ______________________ The *Heisenberg uncertainty principle* says that it is impossible to measure precisely both the position and momentum of a particle at the same time.

Name ____________________

27 Chapter Assessment

Understanding Concepts Part B

Answer the following questions, showing your calculations.

1. The stopping potential of a photocell is 2.5 V. What kinetic energy does the incident light give to the electrons? Give your answer in joules and electron volts.

2. A certain photoelectric surface has a threshold frequency of 4.62×10^{14} Hz.

a. What is the photoelectric work function in joules?

b. The surface is illuminated with light that has a frequency of 5.2×10^{14} Hz. What is the kinetic energy of the electrons ejected from the surface? Give your answer in joules and electron volts.

3. An X ray traveling in a vacuum has a wavelength of 4.2×10^{-12} m. What is the momentum of the wave?

4. What is the de Broglie wavelength of a 1.00-kg object traveling at 45.0 m/s?

Name ______________________

27 Chapter Assessment

Applying Concepts

Answer the following questions, using complete sentences.

1. What conditions must exist to produce a current in a photocell? Does all radiation result in a current? Give a reason for your answer.

____

____

____

2. Compare the predictions of the electromagnetic wave theory and the photon theory when radiation shines on a metal plate. Which one more accurately describes the photoelectric effect?

____

____

____

____

____

____

____

____

3. What happens to the energy of a photon as it interacts with an electron of a metal?

____

____

4. What do both the Compton effect and the photoelectric effect indicate about electromagnetic radiation?

____

5. In the 1920s, a scientist suggested that material particles have wave properties. What evidence was discovered that supports this suggestion?

____

____

____

6. Explain the Heisenberg uncertainty principle.

____

____

Name ______________________________

27 Chapter Assessment

Answer the following questions, showing your calculations.

7. The emission of X rays can be described as an inverse photoelectric effect. What is the potential difference through which an electron accelerates to produce an X ray with a wavelength of 0.10 nm?

8. A potential difference of 200 V accelerates an electron. What is the de Broglie wavelength of the electron? (The mass of an electron is 9.11×10^{-31} kg.)

9. The threshold frequency of sodium is 5.6×10^{14} Hz. If light of frequency 7.8×10^{14} Hz illuminates sodium, electrons are emitted. How fast does one of these electrons travel?

Date ______________ Period ______________ Name ______________________

28 Chapter Assessment

Use with Chapter 28.

The Atom

Understanding Concepts Part A

Write the letter of the choice that best completes the statement or answers the question.

_____ **1.** The results of Rutherford's gold-foil experiment indicated that _____.
- **a.** positive charge is spread throughout the atom
- **b.** positive charge is concentrated in a tiny nucleus
- **c.** electrons exist in the nucleus
- **d.** the nucleus has no electric charge

_____ **2.** Which of the following is characteristic of the emission spectrum for a gas?
- **a.** a continuous band of colors from red through violet
- **b.** a series of separate lines of different colors
- **c.** a band of colors with occasional dark lines
- **d.** bands of color alternating with bands of darkness

_____ **3.** An electron in the ground state _____.
- **a.** is at the lowest energy level
- **b.** can emit energy
- **c.** can remain in that state for only a fraction of a second
- **d.** can move to a lower energy level

_____ **4.** The Bohr model of the atom cannot be used to _____.
- **a.** determine the energy levels of hydrogen
- **b.** account for the chemical properties of hydrogen
- **c.** calculate the ionization energy of hydrogen
- **d.** account for the wave properties of the electron in hydrogen

_____ **5.** The region with a high probability of having an electron is _____.
- **a.** the Bohr orbit
- **b.** the nucleus
- **c.** the electron cloud
- **d.** the absorption band

For each of the statements below, write true *or rewrite the italicized part to make the statement true.*

6. ______________________ The symbol n stands for the principal quantum number.

7. ______________________ The light emitted by lasers is *incoherent*.

8. ______________________ Angular momentum is equal to $2\pi r$.

9. ______________________ When an electron moves from the ground state to an excited state, it *absorbs* energy.

Name ______________________

28 Chapter Assessment

Understanding Concepts Part B

Answer the following questions, showing your calculations.

1. Calculate the radius of the orbit of a hydrogen electron at the $n = 4$ level, given that the radius for the $n = 1$ level is 0.053 nm.

2. What is the energy of a photon emitted when a hydrogen electron drops from the $n = 3$ level to the $n = 2$ level?

3. What are the frequency and wavelength of the photon in problem 2?

4. Heated mercury vapor produces a spectral line with a wavelength of 245 nm. Calculate the energy, in electron volts, of the photon emitted.

5. Calculate the energy of the photons emitted by each of the following three transitions of a hydrogen electron: $n = 5$ to $n = 3$; $n = 6$ to $n = 2$; and $n = 2$ to $n = 1$. Which transition releases the most energetic photon?

Name ______________________

28 Chapter Assessment

Applying Concepts

Answer the following questions, using complete sentences.

1. Explain why line spectra can be thought of as "atomic fingerprints."

2. Distinguish between the ground state and an excited state of an electron.

3. Explain why electrons in an atom do not fall into the nucleus.

4. How does the quantum model of the atom differ from the Bohr model?

5. Explain line spectra in terms of the quantum model of the atom.

6. Why is the word *avalanche* often used to describe the operation of a laser?

Name ______________________________

28 Chapter Assessment

Answer the following questions, showing your calculations.

7. A laser emits light that has a wavelength of 633 nm.

a. What is the energy, in joules, of a photon emitted by the laser?

b. The power of the laser is 0.5 W, and the laser pulses are 20 ms long. How much total energy does a single pulse have? (Recall that power = energy/time, and that 1 W = 1 J/s.)

c. How many photons are in one pulse of the laser?

8. Assume that the Bohr model of the atom is correct. Calculate the velocity of an electron in the first Bohr orbit, given that the mass of an electron is 9.11×10^{-31} kg.

9. Derive a formula to determine an electron's velocity, given its angular momentum and wavelength.

Date ______________ Period ______________ Name ______________________

29 Chapter Assessment

Use with Chapter 29.

Solid State Electronics

Understanding Concepts Part A

Write the letter of the choice that best completes each statement.

_____ **1.** When a potential difference is put across a wire, _____.
- **a.** electron speeds decrease
- **b.** electrons drift slowly toward the positive end of the wire
- **c.** conduction of electricity ceases
- **d.** electron energies lessen

_____ **2.** In a conductor, conductivity increases as _____.
- **a.** temperature decreases
- **b.** temperature increases
- **c.** resistance increases
- **d.** more electrons move into the valence band

_____ **3.** Compared to the forbidden gap in an insulator, the forbidden gap in a semiconductor is _____.
- **a.** much larger
- **b.** slightly larger
- **c.** the same size
- **d.** smaller

_____ **4.** Impurity atoms that increase conductivity are added to a pure semiconductor to produce _____.
- **a.** a conductor
- **b.** an insulator
- **c.** an extrinsic semiconductor
- **d.** an intrinsic semiconductor

_____ **5.** When dopants are added to a semiconductor, the net charge of the material _____.
- **a.** remains zero
- **b.** becomes zero
- **c.** becomes positive
- **d.** becomes negative

_____ **6.** A diode whose holes and free electrons are drawn toward the battery has been _____.
- **a.** forward-biased
- **b.** reverse-biased
- **c.** converted to a transistor
- **d.** given a net charge

_____ **7.** Dopants increase conductivity by _____.
- **a.** creating an electric field
- **b.** decreasing the temperature
- **c.** providing electrons or holes
- **d.** increasing resistance

Name ______________________________

29 Chapter Assessment

For each of the statements below, write true *or* false.

__________ **8.** When two atoms are brought together in a solid, the electric field of one atom affects the field of the other atom.

__________ **9.** A rectifier is a diode used to convert voltage that has only one polarity to AC voltage.

__________ **10.** The highest band that contains electrons is called the valence band.

__________ **11.** When a hole and a free electron combine, their charges cancel each other.

__________ **12.** Miniaturization of integrated circuits does not affect the speed of computers.

Understanding Concepts Part B

Answer the following questions, showing your calculations.

1. Zinc has a density of 7.13 g/cm^3. Its atomic mass is 65.37 g/mol. If zinc has two free electrons per atom, how many free electrons are in a cubic centimeter of zinc?

2. Calculate the density of copper, given that each copper atom contributes one free electron and there are 8.49×10^{22} free e^-/cm^3 Cu. The atomic mass of copper is 63.54 g/mol.

3. Find the number of free electrons per cubic centimeter in silicon at room temperature, given that there are 2×10^{-10} free electrons per atom. The density and molar mass of silicon are 2.33 g/cm^3 and 28.09 g/mol.

4. In a forward-biased silicon diode, the current is 22 mA and the voltage is 0.7 V. If the diode is connected to a battery through a 450-Ω resistor, what is the voltage of the battery?

5. A forward-biased silicon diode is connected to a 12.0-V battery through a resistor. If the current is 12 mA and the voltage is 0.7 V, what is the resistance?

Name ______________________

29 Chapter Assessment

Applying Concepts

Answer the following questions, using complete sentences.

1. Contrast the energy bands of conductors and of insulators.

2. Why is silicon a good semiconductor?

3. Compare and contrast *n*-type semiconductors with *p*-type semiconductors.

4. Why does a diode conduct charges in only one direction easily?

5. How does a supermarket bar-code scanner work?

Name ______________________

29 Chapter Assessment

6. Explain how an *npn* transistor works.

____

____

____

____

____

____

Answer the following questions, showing your calculations.

7. A forward-biased silicon diode is connected to a 6.0-V battery. Also in the circuit are three 220-Ω resistors connected in series. The voltage in the circuit is 0.7 V. What is the current?

8. Intrinsic silicon has 1×10^{13} free electrons per centimeter. A doped silicon crystal has 4.99×10^{22} silicon atoms per cubic centimeter. The silicon is doped with arsenic so that one in every 1×10^{7} silicon atoms is replaced by an arsenic atom.

   a. If each arsenic atom donates one electron to the conduction band, what is the density of free electrons in the resulting semiconductor?

   b. By what ratio is the free-electron density in the doped silicon greater than that of intrinsic silicon?

   c. Does conduction in the doped silicon take place mainly by means of thermally freed electrons of the silicon itself or by means of the arsenic-donated electrons? Give a reason for your answer.

____

____

Date ______________ Period ______________ Name ______________________

30 Chapter Assessment

Use with Chapter 30.

The Nucleus

Understanding Concepts Part A

Write the letter of the choice that best completes the statement or answers the question.

_____ **1.** An atom's atomic number refers to the _____.
- **a.** number of neutrons in a atom
- **b.** number of protons in a atom
- **c.** half the atom's atomic mass
- **d.** number of isotopes of the atom

_____ **2.** The mass number of an atom is equal to _____.
- **a.** the sum of its protons and electrons
- **b.** twice its number of neutrons
- **c.** half its atomic number
- **d.** the sum of its protons and neutrons

_____ **3.** All nuclides of an element have _____.
- **a.** different numbers of protons
- **b.** the same number of neutrons
- **c.** the same number of protons
- **d.** different numbers of electrons

_____ **4.** The number of decays per second in a sample of radioactive material is its _____.
- **a.** half-life
- **b.** activity
- **c.** gamma decay
- **d.** nuclear reaction

_____ **5.** Which type of radioactive decay occurs when a neutron changes to a proton within the nucleus?
- **a.** alpha decay
- **b.** beta decay
- **c.** gamma decay
- **d.** positron decay

_____ **6.** The time required for half the atoms in a given quantity of a radioactive isotope to decay is the _____ of that element.
- **a.** half-life
- **b.** activity
- **c.** ionization rate
- **d.** weak interaction

_____ **7.** Which of the following is a type of particle accelerator?
- **a.** Geiger-Mueller tube
- **b.** Wilson cloud chamber
- **c.** synchrotron
- **d.** vacuum container

_____ **8.** Physicists believe that quarks make up _____.
- **a.** neutrons and electrons
- **b.** neutrinos and neutrons
- **c.** protons and electrons
- **d.** protons and neutrons

Name ______________________________

30 Chapter Assessment

Understanding Concepts Part B

Answer the following questions.

1. The atomic mass of the most abundant isotope of bismuth is about 209 u. The atomic number of bismuth is 83. How many neutrons does an atom of this isotope of bismuth have?

2. A radium atom, $^{224}_{88}\text{Ra}$, decays to radon, Rn, by emitting an α particle.

   a. Write a nuclear equation for this transmutation.

   b. What is the charge of the new nucleus?

   ____

3. An atom of plutonium, $^{243}_{94}\text{Pu}$, emits a β particle when its nucleus decays to americium, Am.

   a. Write a nuclear equation for this transmutation.

   b. Indicate the number of protons and neutrons in the americium nucleus.

   ____

4. Complete the following equations.

   a. $^{253}_{99}\text{Es} + {}^{4}_{2}\text{He} \rightarrow {}^{256}_{101}\text{Md} +$ ______________

   b. $^{238}_{92}\text{U} + 17\ {}^{1}_{0}\text{n} \rightarrow {}^{255}_{100}\text{Fm} +$ ______________

   c. $^{4}_{2}\text{He} + {}^{9}_{4}\text{Be} \rightarrow$ ______________ $+ {}^{1}_{0}\text{n}$

5. If a radioactive sample has an activity of 24 decays/s, what will the activity be after two half-lives have passed?

Name ______________________

30 Chapter Assessment

Applying Concepts

Answer the following questions using complete sentences.

1. How can you calculate the mass of a nucleus?

2. Compare the penetrating abilities of alpha, beta, and gamma radiation. Give examples of shields capable of stopping the different types of radiation.

3. Describe the effect gamma decay has on the mass number and atomic number of an atom.

4. Compare the number of protons, neutrons, and electrons found in two neutral isotopes of the same element.

Name ______________________

30 Chapter Assessment

5. Since the total number of nuclear particles during a nuclear reaction stays the same, what must be true of an equation representing such a reaction?

6. Why can't a linear accelerator speed up neutrons?

7. Use the quark model to explain why a proton has a positive charge and a neutron has no charge.

Name ______________________

30 Chapter Assessment

Answer the following questions.

8. Geologists use the radioactive decay of $^{40}_{19}K$ to determine the ages of certain minerals. Assume that when the mineral is formed, $^{40}_{19}K$ is trapped in a crystal, but none of its decay products exist in the mineral at the time. The half-life of $^{40}_{19}K$ is 1.3×10^9 years. The decay products of $^{40}_{19}K$ are $^{40}_{18}Ar$ (12%) and $^{40}_{20}Ca$ (88%). An analysis of the mineral reveals that the ratio of $^{40}_{19}K$ to $^{40}_{18}Ar$ to $^{40}_{20}Ca$ is approximately 25:9:66.

a. What is the approximate age of the mineral? Give a reason for your answer.

____

____

____

____

____

b. Write an equation for the transmutation of $^{40}_{19}K$ to $^{40}_{20}Ca$.

c. Write an equation for the transmutation of $^{40}_{19}K$ to $^{40}_{18}Ar$.

9. The half-life of $^{35}_{17}Cl$ is 2.5 s. It decays to sulfur, S, through emission of a positron.

a. If the mass of a sample of $^{35}_{17}Cl$ is 16 g, how much will remain after 15 s?

b. Write a complete equation to represent the decay of $^{35}_{17}Cl$.

Name ______________________

30 Chapter Assessment

10. The half-life of $^{52}_{25}Mn$ is 5.6 days. What was the original mass of $^{52}_{25}Mn$ if, after 50.4 days, 1.20 g are found?

11. In nature, $^{238}_{92}U$ decay goes through 14 steps until a stable nuclide forms. The series below shows these 14 steps. Some information is missing at each step. Fill in the missing subscripts and superscripts for each nuclide. Label each arrow as alpha or beta decay.

$^{238}_{92}U \longrightarrow {}^{234}_{90}Th \longrightarrow {}^{234}_{91}Pa \longrightarrow {}^{234}_{90}U \longrightarrow {}^{230}_{90}Th \longrightarrow {}^{226}_{88}Ra \longrightarrow$

$^{222}_{86}Rn \longrightarrow {}^{218}_{84}Po \longrightarrow {}^{214}_{82}Pb \longrightarrow {}^{214}_{83}Bi \longrightarrow {}^{214}_{84}Po \longrightarrow {}^{210}_{82}Pb \longrightarrow$

$^{210}_{83}Bi \longrightarrow {}^{210}_{84}Po \longrightarrow {}^{206}_{82}Pb$

Date ________________ Period ________________ Name ________________________________

31 Chapter Assessment

Use with Chapter 31.

Nuclear Applications

Understanding Concepts Part A

For each of the statements below, write true *or rewrite the italicized part to make the statement true.*

1. ______________________ The range over which the *weak force* acts is about 1.3×10^{-15} m.

2. ______________________ Binding energy is the amount of energy required to separate the nucleus into individual *nucleons.*

3. ______________________ The binding energy of the nucleus is *positive.*

4. ______________________ The mass of the assembled nucleus is *more* than the sum of the masses of the nucleons that compose it.

5. ______________________ In a nuclear reaction, the binding energy before the reaction is *less* than it is after the reaction.

6. ______________________ Radioactive isotopes *cannot* be formed artificially.

Write the letter of the choice that best completes each statement.

_____ **7.** The detection of _____ indicates the movement of isotopes through the body.
- **a.** charge
- **b.** decay products
- **c.** light
- **d.** changes in mass

_____ **8.** Nuclear fission refers to _____.
- **a.** a chemical reaction in which an atom dissociates into ions.
- **b.** the combining of two nuclei
- **c.** the division of a nucleus
- **d.** the separation of two atoms

_____ **9.** A moderator in a nuclear reactor decreases the speed of _____.
- **a.** neutrons
- **b.** electrons
- **c.** protons
- **d.** neutrinos

_____ **10.** The rate of a chain reaction is changed by _____.
- **a.** moderators
- **b.** control rods
- **c.** nucleons
- **d.** uranium rods

_____ **11.** In the fusion process in the sun, a helium nucleus forms from the _____.
- **a.** fusion of four hydrogen nuclei
- **b.** fusion of four neutrons
- **c.** transmutation of a hydrogen nucleus
- **d.** fission of a beryllium nucleus

Name ______________________________

31 Chapter Assessment

Understanding Concepts Part B

Answer the following questions, showing your calculations.

1. The nuclear mass of $^{101}_{44}Ru$ is 100.9 u.

a. What is the ruthenium's mass defect?

b. What is the ruthenium's binding energy in MeV?

2. Write the nuclear equation for beta decay: $^{94}_{43}Tc$ to ruthenium, Ru

3. Write the nuclear equation for alpha decay: $^{144}_{60}Nd$ to cesium, Ce

4. Write an equation for the following change: $^{174}_{73}Ta$ emits a positron, and forms hafnium, Hf.

5. The human thyroid gland uses iodine to produce vital hormones. Based on this fact, scientists have devised ways of using radioactive $^{131}_{53}I$ to measure the functions of the thyroid.

a. $^{131}_{53}I$ decays to xenon, Xe, by emission of a β particle. What isotope of xenon is formed?

____

b. Write the equation for this reaction.

c. The half-life of $^{131}_{53}I$ is approximately eight days. If a patient is given a 6.0-mg dose of $^{131}_{53}I$ on a Monday, how much $^{131}_{53}I$ will remain in the patient's body eight days later?

Name ______________________

31 Chapter Assessment

Applying Concepts

Answer the following questions, using complete sentences.

1. Explain how the mass defect relates to the equation $E = mc^2$.

____

____

2. Under what circumstances is energy released by a nuclear reaction?

____

____

3. How did Lise Meitner and Otto Frisch explain the production of small atoms, such as barium, from uranium atoms?

____

____

4. What is the function of a moderator in a nuclear reactor?

____

____

____

____

____

5. What is the Cerenkov effect and what causes it?

____

____

____

6. Compare the amount of energy released when a dynamite molecule reacts chemically to the amount of energy released by the fusion of a helium nucleus.

____

____

____

____

Name ______________________

31 Chapter Assessment

7. Describe how a magnetic field is used to control fusion.

____

____

____

____

Answer the following questions, showing your calculations.

8. A sample of a pure isotope of berkelium, Bk, decays to produce an isotope of curium, ${}^{248}_{96}Cm$. In this process, the nucleus captures an orbiting electron.

a. Write an equation for this decay.

b. What was the original isotope of berkelium?

____

9. The energy released in the fission of one atom of ${}^{239}_{94}Pu$ is 1.6 MeV.

a. How many atoms are in 2.0 kg of pure ${}^{239}_{94}Pu$?

b. How much energy would be released if all these atoms underwent fission?

10. An ${}^{252}_{99}Es$ nucleus (mass = 252.0829 u) decays to ${}^{248}_{97}Bk$ (mass = 248.0702 u) by emitting an α particle (mass = 4.0026 u) with a kinetic energy of 6.64 MeV. What is the kinetic energy of the berkelium nucleus?

11. If 1.806×10^{24} atoms of ${}^{235}_{92}U$ undergo fission and produce 1.0×10^{13} J, how much energy is produced per kilogram of ${}^{235}_{92}U$?

Date ______ Period ______ Name ______

1 Chapter Assessment

Use with Chapter 1.

What is physics?

Understanding Concepts

Write the letter of the choice that best completes each statement.

__d__ **1.** Physics is the study of ____.

- **a.** matter and cells
- **b.** energy and heat
- **c.** energy and atoms
- **d.** matter and energy

__b__ **2.** Ancient Greek scholars believed that all matter on or near Earth was made of ____ elements.

- **a.** 1
- **b.** 4
- **c.** 100
- **d.** 111

__d__ **3.** Ancient Greek scholars believed that celestial objects were formed from ____.

- **a.** air
- **b.** fire
- **c.** light
- **d.** quintessence

__c__ **4.** ____ is considered to be the father of modern experimental science.

- **a.** Albert Einstein
- **b.** Aristotle
- **c.** Galileo Galilei
- **d.** Louis Pasteur

__d__ **5.** The first successful landing and operation of a vehicle on the surface of Mars took place during the ____ mission.

- **a.** *Global Surveyor*
- **b.** *Mariner 9*
- **c.** *Phobos 2*
- **d.** *Viking 1*

Name ______

1 Chapter Assessment

For each of the statements below, write true *or rewrite the italicized part to make the statement true.*

6. Planets were called wanderers by ancient people because their *brightness* differed from the stars.
motion

7. Greek philosophers thought that *motion* occurred because an element traveled in a straight line to its own natural place.
true

8. Galileo was the first to discover that the moon had *an atmosphere.*
mountains

9. Galileo argued that the planets circled *Earth.*
the sun

10. In the scientific method, conclusions are tested to find out whether they are *valid.*
true

Applying Concepts

Answer the following questions, using complete sentences.

1. Describe how physicists study problems in an organized way.
Physicists make observations, do experiments, and create models or theories to answer questions.

2. What are the three functions of a scientific explanation?
The three functions are to describe many different events, make predictions, and lead to a better understanding of the universe.

3. What is similar in the ways scientists study problems?
All scientists study problems in an organized way. They combine systematic experimentation with careful measurements and analysis of results, and then draw conclusions. The conclusions are then tested for validity.

4. What information might scientists learn from studying the Martian atmosphere?
Scientists may learn about the formation and evolution of the solar system and conditions that could lead to dramatic climatic or atmospheric changes on Earth.

Name ____________

1 Chapter Assessment

5. What are some benefits of working on a team?
Individual backgrounds and experiences can be joined. The team can accomplish more than an individual and so the rewards can be greater; it is stimulating to share ideas and experiences.

6. Describe two applications that resulted from the work of physicists.
Answers may vary. They could include computers, lasers, radar, thin-film materials, and composites.

Date ________ Period ________ Name ____________

2 Chapter Assessment

Use with Chapter 2.

A Mathematical Toolkit

Understanding Concepts Part A

Write the letter of the choice that best completes each statement.

c 1. The base SI unit for time is the _____.
- a. minute
- b. day
- c. second
- d. hour

a 2. In scientific notation, a number between 1 and 10 is multiplied by _____.
- a. a whole-number power of 10
- b. a fraction
- c. 10
- d. any whole number

b 3. The metric prefix that means 1/1 000 000 000 is _____.
- a. pico
- b. nano
- c. centi
- d. giga

a 4. To avoid parallax errors, laboratory instruments should be read _____.
- a. at eye level
- b. from the side
- c. below eye level
- d. at all of these positions

d 5. The slope of a straight-line graph is the rise _____ the run.
- a. added to
- b. subtracted from
- c. multiplied by
- d. divided by

For each of the statements below, write true *or rewrite the italicized part to make the statement true.*

6. **derived** The unit of speed, m/s, is an example of a *base* unit.

7. **precision** The degree of exactness to which the measurement of a quantity can be reproduced is called *accuracy*.

8. **true** A variable that can be manipulated in an experiment is the *independent* variable.

9. **independent** When constructing a graph from data, the range of the *x*-axis is determined by the range of the *dependent* variable.

10. **true** A graph that is a hyperbola represents an *inverse* relationship.

11. **quadratic** A graph that is a parabola represents a *linear* relationship.

Name ______

2 Chapter Assessment

Understanding Concepts Part B

Answer the following questions.

1. Express the measurements in scientific notation.
   a. 142 000 s **1.42×10^5 s**
   b. 0.008 09 kg **8.09×10^{-3} kg**
   c. 501 000 000 m **5.01×10^8 m**
2. Simplify the expressions. Give your answers in scientific notation, using the correct number of significant digits.
   a. $(2 \times 10^6 \text{ m})(5 \times 10^5 \text{ m})$ **1×10^{12} m^2**
   b. $(12 \times 10^6 \text{ m})/(4 \times 10^2 \text{ s})$ **3×10^4 m/s**
   c. $(5.06 \times 10^2 \text{ m}) + (8.124 \text{ km})$ **8.63×10^3 m**
3. Describe the relationship between the variables shown in the graph below. Identify the general equation that is used to represent this type of relationship.

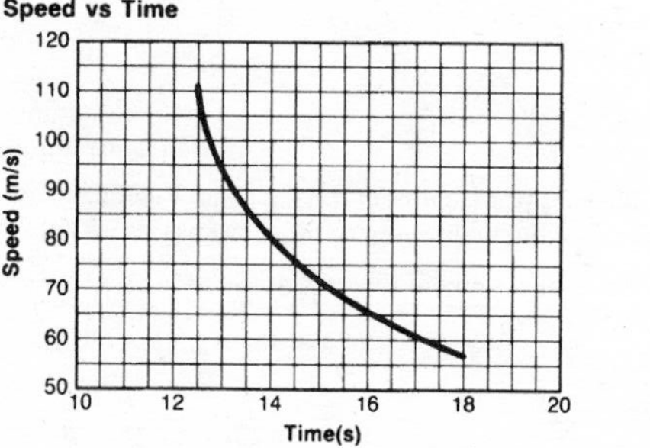

Time varies with the inverse of the speed. The graph shows an inverse relationship between the variables, $y = \frac{a}{x}$.

4. Identify the slope and y-intercept of the equation
   Fahrenheit Temperature = (1.8°F/°C)(*Celsius Temperature*) + 32°F.
   m = 1.8°F/°C, y-intercept = 32°F

Name ______

2 Chapter Assessment

Applying Concepts

Answer the following questions, using complete sentences.

1. Describe the relationship between base units and derived units.
   Base units can be combined to describe other quantities. Derived units are combinations of base units.
2. Which of the following is a more precise measurement, the length of a tabletop measured with a stick calibrated in centimeters as shown on the left, or the length measured with a stick calibrated in millimeters as shown on the right? Give a reason for your answer.

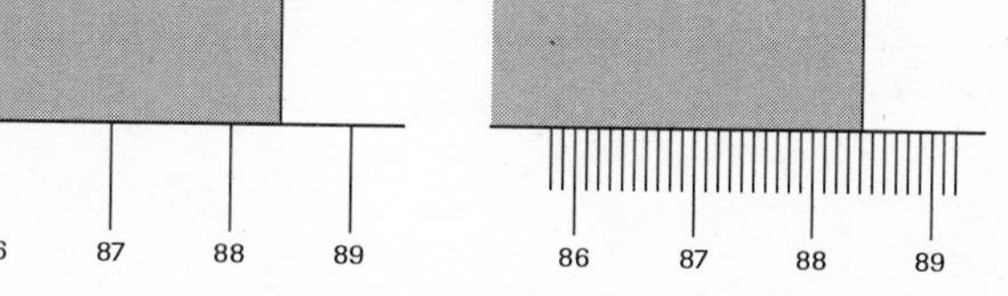

Because the millimeter is the smaller unit, the length of the tabletop measured in millimeters is more precise.

3. Express the measurements in the diagram above in centimeters. **88.5 cm, 88.41 cm**
4. Explain the difference between accuracy and precision.
   Precision is the degree of exactness used in measuring a quantity. Accuracy is the extent to which the measured and accepted values of a quantity agree.
5. Give the number of significant digits in each measurement.
   a. 3809 m **4** b. 9.013 m **4** c. 0.0045 m **2**
6. Which of the following measurements contains zeros that are *not* significant? Give a reason for your answer.
   3.050×10^5 mm 0.0053 m 45.020 cm 101.20 g
   The only measurement with zeros that are not significant is 0.0053 m; the zeros are used solely for spacing the decimal point. In all the other measurements, the zeros after the decimal point are significant.
7. How are independent and dependent variables related? Identify the graph axis on which each type of variable would be plotted.
   The independent variable is a manipulated variable. It is graphed on the *x*-axis. A dependent variable changes as a result of a change in an independent variable. It is plotted on the *y*-axis.

Name ____________

2 Chapter Assessment

Answer the following questions, showing your calculations.

8. The total mass of four containers is 5.000 kg. If the mass of container A is 256 mg, container B is 5117 cg, and container C is 382 g, what is the mass of container D?

D = 5.000 kg − A − B − C

= 5.000 kg − 0.000 256 kg − 0.051 17 kg − 0.382 kg

= 4.567 kg

9. Show that the measurements in each pair are equivalent.

a. 0.002 35 Ts, 2350 Ms

0.002 35 Ts = 2.35 × 10^{-3} Ts × 10^{12} s/Ts = 2.35 × 10^{9} s

2.35 × 10^{3} Ms × 10^{6} s/Ms = 2.35 × 10^{9} s

b. 5687 nm , 0.000 056 87 dm

5687 nm = 5.687 × 10^{3} nm × 10^{-9} m/nm = 5.687 × 10^{-6} m

0.000 056 87 dm = 5.687 × 10^{-5} dm × 10^{-1} m/dm = 5.687 × 10^{-6} m

10. The results of a class experiment investigating the relationship between mass and acceleration are shown in the table below. The force applied to each mass remained constant.

Mass (kg)	Acceleration (m/s^2)
0.5	6.0
1.0	3.0
1.5	2.0
2.0	1.5
2.5	1.2
3.0	1.0

a. Plot the values given and draw the curve that best fits the points.

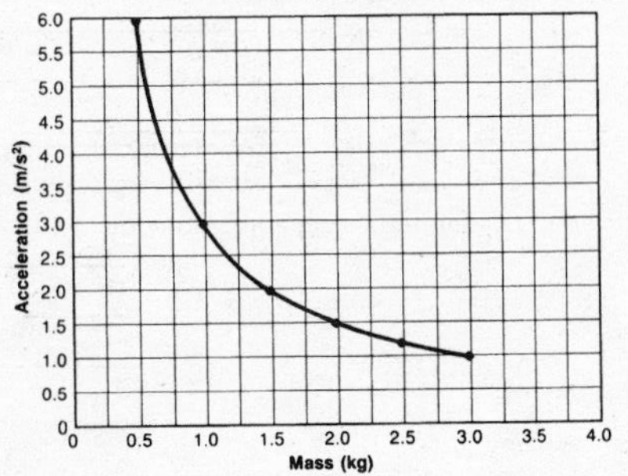

b. Describe the resulting curve.

The graph is a hyperbola.

c. What is the relationship between mass and the acceleration produced by a constant force?

The relationship between the variables is inverse.

d. What is the general equation for the relationship shown in the graph?

a = k/m, where k is a constant, m is mass, and a is acceleration

Date ________ Period ________ Name ____________

3 Chapter Assessment

Use with Chapter 3.

Describing Motion

Understanding Concepts Part A

For each of the statements below, write true *or rewrite the italicized part to make the statement true.*

1. **true** A series of images of an object that records its position after equal time intervals is called a motion diagram.
2. **at rest** No change in the position of an object in successive frames of a motion diagram is an operational definition of an object *with a positive acceleration*.
3. **much less than** A particle model can be used to represent a moving object if the size of the object is *much greater than* the distance it moves.
4. **true** To study the motion of a sprinter, the *finish line* would be one choice for the origin of a coordinate system.
5. **Diagram D** Each of the four motion diagrams below shows the position of an object at successive 1-s time intervals. *Diagram A* shows an object with a constant positive acceleration.

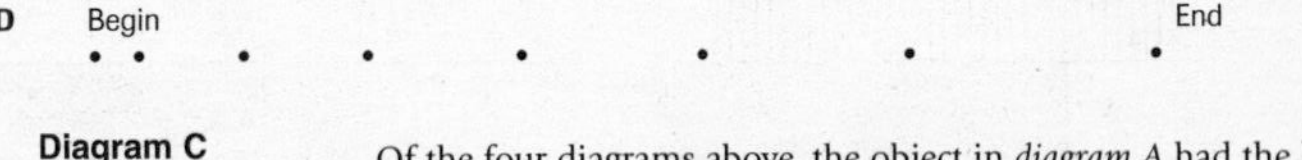

6. **Diagram C** Of the four diagrams above, the object in *diagram A* had the largest average velocity for any time interval.
7. **speed** Displacement is to distance as velocity is to *acceleration*.
8. **true** The *displacement* of an object is equal to the product of its average velocity and the time interval.
9. **true** The ratio of the change in average velocity to the time interval in which the change is made is defined as *average acceleration*.
10. **speeding up** If a truck has a negative velocity and a negative acceleration, the truck is *slowing down* in the negative direction.

Name ______________________

3 Chapter Assessment

Understanding Concepts Part B

Create pictorial and physical models for each of the following problems. Do not solve the problem.

1. A hockey puck's average velocity is 22 m/s. What is its displacement in 6.0 s?

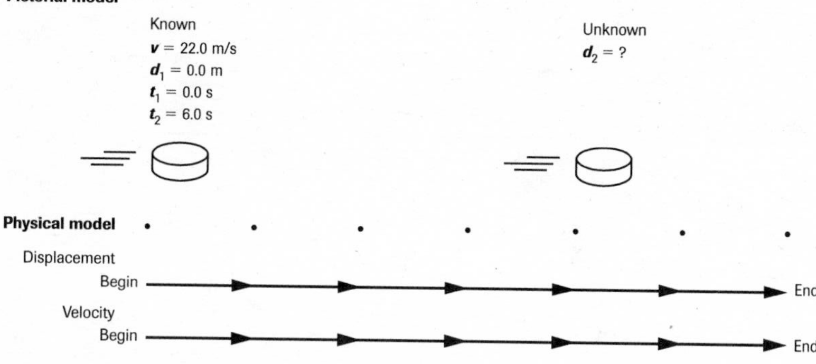

2. A car maintains an acceleration of 0.6 m/s² from rest for 5.0 s. How far does it move in this time?

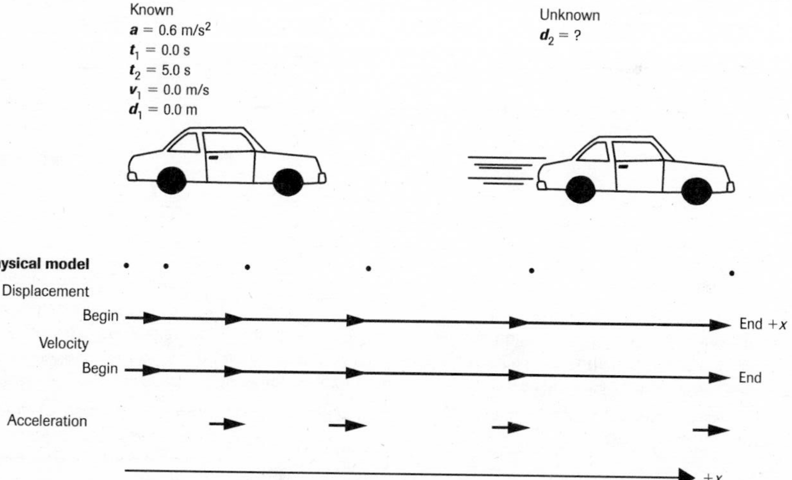

Name ______________________

3 Chapter Assessment

Applying Concepts

Answer the following questions, using complete sentences.

1. When looking at an object recorded in successive frames by a camcorder, how can you determine if the object is moving?
   The object's position changes relative to stationary objects in the background.

2. How can you operationally define the constant speed of an object, using successive frames of a camcorder?
   Constant speed occurs when the distance between positions of the object in successive frames is the same.

3. How can an object have a *negative* position?
   An object can have a negative position if it is to the left of the origin of an *x*-axis chosen to extend in a positive direction to the right.

4. From observing successive camcorder frames in which two objects are moving, how can you determine which of the two objects is moving faster?
   The object that is moving faster has greater distance between successive images.

5. Explain how a moving object could have a motion diagram that is the same as that of an object at rest.
   The object is moving back and forth during the time interval between successive frames in such a way that it is always at the same position in each successive frame.

6. My house is 5 minutes away from school by bike. How am I operationally defining distance?
   You are operationally defining the distance as the displacement undergone by a person biking at a normal speed for 5 minutes.

7. Explain what is meant by an object having an acceleration of +8 m/s².
   The velocity of the object is increasing by 8 m/s in the positive direction during each second of travel.

Name ______________________

3 Chapter Assessment

Set up the pictorial and physical models for each of the following problems. You need not solve the problem.

8. A tennis ball is released at the top of a 2-m ramp and rolls down with an acceleration of 1.0 m/s^2. The ball reaches the end of the ramp in 2.0 s and rolls onto the floor. If the ball experiences an average acceleration of -0.5 m/s^2 as it rolls along the floor, how far from the end of the ramp will the ball stop?

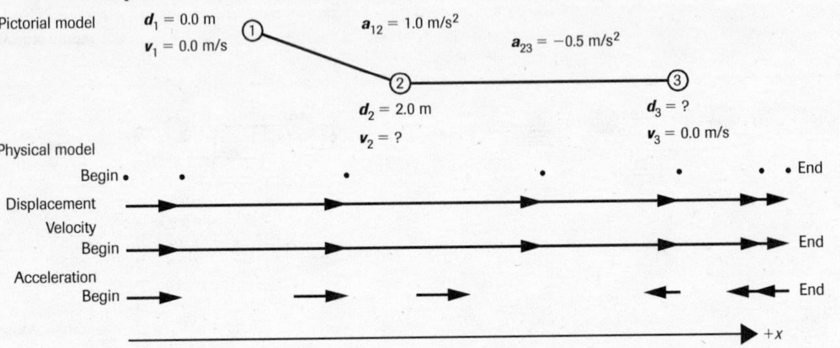

9. While jogging, Maria sees Jason 15 m ahead of her, walking in the same direction. If Maria is jogging at 5.0 m/s and Jason is walking at 2.0 m/s, how far will Maria have to jog before catching up to Jason?

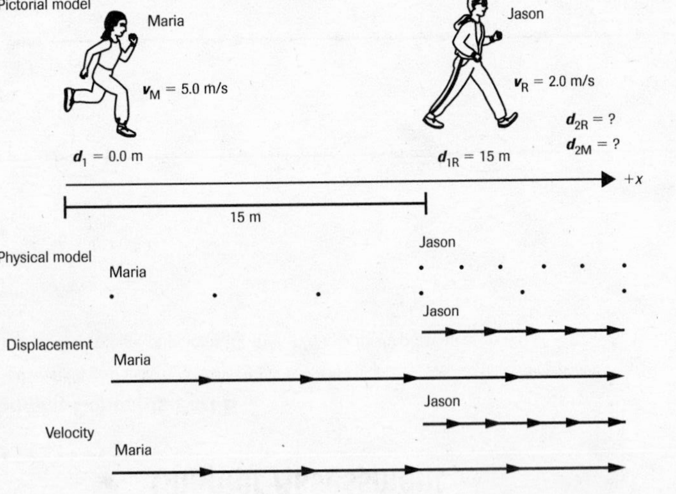

Date ____________ Period ____________ Name ______________________

4 Chapter Assessment

Use with Chapter 4.

Vector Addition

Understanding Concepts Part A

Write the letter of the choice that best completes the statement or answers the question.

c **1.** The downstream velocity of a river that flows south _____ a boat's eastward velocity.
- **a.** slightly increases
- **b.** slightly decreases
- **c.** has no effect on

b **2.** When adding vectors graphically, the direction and length of each vector must _____.
- **a.** be similar to the direction and length of the resultant.
- **b.** not be changed
- **c.** be reversed

a **3.** You walked 10 km west and then ran 10 km north. During each part of the journey, the _____ was the same.
- **a.** distance
- **b.** displacement
- **c.** speed
- **d.** velocity

c **4.** The magnitude of the resultant vector is _____.
- **a.** the difference between the magnitudes of the original vectors
- **b.** the sum of the magnitudes of the original vectors
- **c.** calculated using the Law of Cosines

b **5.** A runner is 5.0 km east of another runner, who is 5.0 km east of a parking lot. Where is the first runner with respect to the parking lot?
- **a.** 5 km east of the lot
- **b.** 10 km east of the lot
- **c.** at the lot
- **d.** −5 km east of the lot

For each situation below, write the letter of the matching item.

c **6.** A hiker walks 15 km due east, then heads due north for 8 km. What is the direction of the resultant vector?

b **7.** After a bike ride, your displacement is 10 km, 30° east of north. In which direction is your displacement greatest?

c **8.** A swimmer wants to swim due east in a stream that flows due south. In which direction should the swimmer swim?

f **9.** The vertical and horizontal components of a vector are both negative values in a coordinate system. If the vector is in quadrant III, in what direction does the *x*-axis point?

- **a.** east
- **b.** north
- **c.** northeast
- **d.** south
- **e.** southeast
- **f.** west

Name ____________

4 Chapter Assessment

Understanding Concepts Part B

Answer the following questions, showing your calculations.

1. You exercised by walking for 15 minutes on a treadmill that has a level track that moves at a velocity of −4 km/h.
   a. What was your velocity relative to the treadmill track while you were exercising?
   4 km/h
   b. What was your velocity relative to the floor while you were exercising?
   0 km/h
   c. What was your total displacement relative to the treadmill track when you finished exercising?
   1 km
   d. What was your total displacement relative to the floor when you finished exercising?
   0 km
2. A rubber ball strikes a wall at a velocity of 30 km/h and rebounds with a velocity of −20 km/h. What is the change of velocity of the ball?
   $$\Delta v = v_2 - v_1 = -20\,\frac{km}{h} - 30\,\frac{km}{h} = -50\,\frac{km}{h}$$
3. A hot-air balloon is ascending straight upward at 30 km/h in air that is blowing horizontally at 8 km/h. What is the horizontal velocity of the balloon relative to the wind?
   0 km/h
4. Find the components of the velocity of a car that is moving at 30.0 km/h in a direction 35.0° north of east.
   $v_x = v \cos\theta$ $= (30.0\ km/h)(0.8192)$ $= 24.6\ km/h$
   $v_y = v \sin\theta$ $= (30.0\ km/h)(0.5736)$ $= 17.2\ km/h$
5. A runner jogs 8.0 km west, turns and jogs 10.0 km south, and then jogs 7.0 km north at a constant speed. Graphically determine the magnitude and direction of the jogger's displacement.

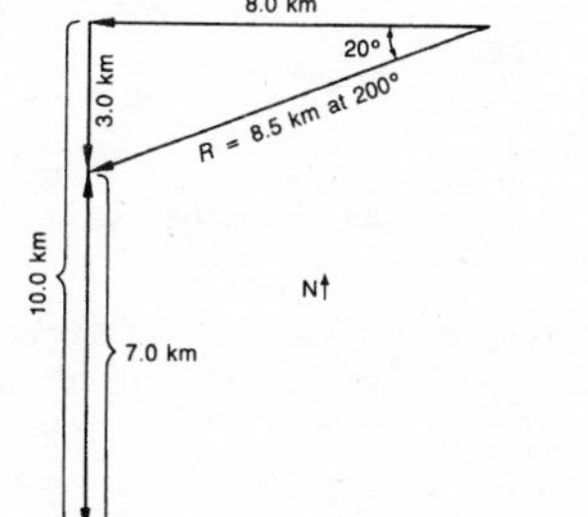

Name ____________

4 Chapter Assessment

Applying Concepts

Answer these questions, showing your calculations.

1. Describe how to add two perpendicular velocity vectors.
   Answers may use algebraic or graphical method; a sample follows. Each velocity vector is drawn to scale. The tail of the second vector is placed at the head of the first vector. The resultant vector is drawn from the tail of the first vector to the head of the second vector.
2. Describe how to add two vectors, using their components.
   Determine the *x*- and *y*-components of each vector from the projections of the vector onto the *x*- and *y*-axes. Find the sum of the two *x*-components and the sum of the two *y*-components. Determine the resultant from the two components by using the Pythagorean relationship, and the direction by using the tangent function.
3. A problem involves a box placed on an incline. A coordinate system is chosen so that the *x*-axis is parallel to the incline and the positive direction points up the incline.
   a. Describe the motion of the box if it has a negative velocity in this coordinate system.
   The box is moving down the incline.
   b. Describe the motion of the box if it has a positive velocity at 90.0° in this coordinate system.
   The box is moving perpendicularly upward off the surface of the incline.
4. The diagram below shows two vectors representing the route a person took from home. Draw the vector that indicates the most direct route home.

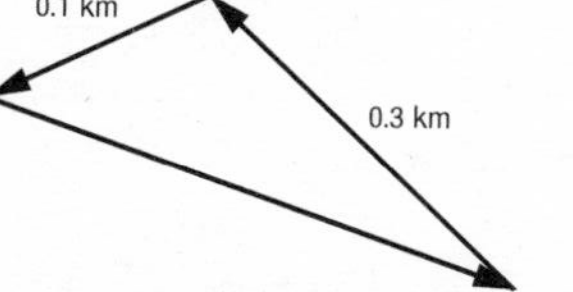

5. Two displacement vectors have equal magnitudes of 8 km. Describe the two vectors if their sum has the following values: 0 km, 8 km, and 16 km.
   0 km tells you that the displacements are in opposite directions. 8 km tells you that the second displacement is at 60.0° with respect to the first. 16 km tells you that the displacements are in the same direction.

Name ____________

4 Chapter Assessment

6. Determine trigonometrically the magnitude and direction of the velocity of a plane that is flying west at 100.0 km/h with respect to the air while the wind is blowing toward the north at 65.0 km/h relative to the ground.

$v_g^2 = v_p^2 + v_w^2 = (100.0 \text{ km/h})^2 + (65.0 \text{ km/h})^2$

$= (1.423 \times 10^4 \text{ km/h})^2$

$v_g = 119 \text{ km/h}$

$\tan\theta = \frac{v_w}{v_p}$

$= \frac{65.0 \text{ km/h}}{-100.0 \text{ km/h}} = -0.650$

$\theta = 180.0° - 33.0° = 147°$ or 33.0° north of we

7. A pilot wants to fly a plane at 500.0 km/h, directly north. The wind is blowing at 90.0 km/h from the east. Find the magnitude and direction of the course the pilot should fly.

$v_g^2 = v_p^2 + v_w^2$

$= (500.0 \text{ km/h})^2 + (90.0 \text{ km/h})^2$

$v_g = 508 \text{ km/h}$

$\tan\theta = \frac{v_p}{v_w}$

$= \frac{500.0 \text{ km/h}}{90.0 \text{ km/h}} = 5.56$

$\theta = 79.8°$ north of east

8. A soccer ball is rolling east at an average velocity of 6.0 m/s when a kick deflects it to the north at an average velocity of 7.0 m/s. What is the magnitude and direction of the ball's change of velocity?

$(\Delta v)^2 = v_2^2 + v_1^2 = (7.0 \text{ m/s})^2 + (6.0 \text{ m/s})^2$

$= (85 \text{ m/s})^2$

$\Delta v = 9.2 \text{ m/s}$

$\tan\theta = \frac{6.0 \text{ m/s}}{7.0 \text{ m/s}} = 0.857$

$\theta = 41°$ west of north

9. The directions to locate a buried time capsule tell you to walk 50 paces west from the front door of your school, turn 80° to the left, and walk 40 more paces. What is the magnitude of the capsule's displacement from the door of the school?

$R^2 = A^2 + B^2 - 2AB\cos\theta$

$= (50 \text{ paces})^2 + (40 \text{ paces})^2 - 2(50 \text{ paces})(40 \text{ paces})\cos(180° - 80°)$

$= 2500 \text{ paces}^2 + 1600 \text{ paces}^2 - 4000 \text{ paces}^2(-0.174)$

$R = 69 \text{ paces}$

Date ____________ Period ____________ Name ____________

5 Chapter Assessment

Use with Chapter 5.

A Mathematical Model of Motion

Understanding Concepts Part A

For each description on the left, write the letter of the matching item.

b 1. the slope of the tangent to a curve of a position-time graph

e 2. change of position of an object

h 3. displacement divided by the time interval during which the displacement took place

c 4. motion in which equal displacements take place in successive equal time periods

d 5. change of velocity divided by the time interval during which the change took place

f 6. the slope of the tangent to a curve of a velocity-time graph

a 7. motion that is described by a line of constant slope on a velocity-time graph

g 8. the constant acceleration that acts on falling bodies

a. constant acceleration
b. instantaneous velocity
c. uniform motion
d. average acceleration
e. displacement
f. instantaneous acceleration
g. acceleration due to gravity
h. average velocity

For each of the statements below, write true *or rewrite the italicized part to make the statement true.*

9. On a position-time graph, the average velocity equals the *run multiplied* by the rise.
rise divided by the run

10. A child drops a ball. The instantaneous velocity of the ball as the child lets go is *zero*.
true

11. A child drops a ball. The instantaneous acceleration of the ball as the child lets go is *zero*.
9.8 m/s²

12 A toy rocket is launched vertically upward. When the rocket reaches its highest point, its velocity is *at its maximum*.
zero

Name ______________________

5 Chapter Assessment

Understanding Concepts Part B

1. A skateboard rider starts from rest and maintains a constant acceleration of +0.50 m/s^2 for 8.4 s. What is the rider's displacement during this time?

$d = v_0t + \frac{1}{2}at^2$

$= (0 \text{ m/s})(8.4 \text{ s}) + \frac{1}{2}(0.50 \text{ m/s}^2)(8.4 \text{ s})^2$

$= 18 \text{ m}$

2. A sports car can move 100.0 m in the first 4.5 s of uniform acceleration. Find the car's acceleration.

$d = v_0t + \frac{1}{2}at^2$ $\quad a = \frac{2(d - v_0t)}{t^2}$

$= \frac{2((100.0 \text{ m}) - (0 \text{ m/s})(4.5 \text{ s}))}{(4.5 \text{ s})^2}$

$= 9.9 \text{ m/s}^2$

3. A rolling ball has an initial velocity of −1.6 m/s.

   a. If the ball has a constant acceleration of −0.33 m/s^2, what is its velocity after 3.6 s?

   $v = v_0 + at$

   $= -1.6 \text{ m/s} + (-0.33 \text{ m/s}^2)(3.6 \text{ s})$

   $= -2.8 \text{ m/s}$

   b. How far did it travel in this time?

   $d = v_0t + \frac{1}{2}at^2$

   $= (-1.6 \text{ m/s})(3.6 \text{ s}) + \frac{1}{2}(-0.33 \text{ m/s}^2)(3.6 \text{ s})^2$

   $= -7.9 \text{ m}$

Name ______________________

5 Chapter Assessment

4. Use the data below to make a velocity-time graph.

Time (s)	Velocity (m/s)	Time (s)	Velocity (m/s)
0.0	20.0	7.0	33.0
2.0	20.0	8.0	40.0
4.0	20.0	10.0	25.0
5.0	20.0	11.0	17.5
6.0	26.0	12.0	10.0

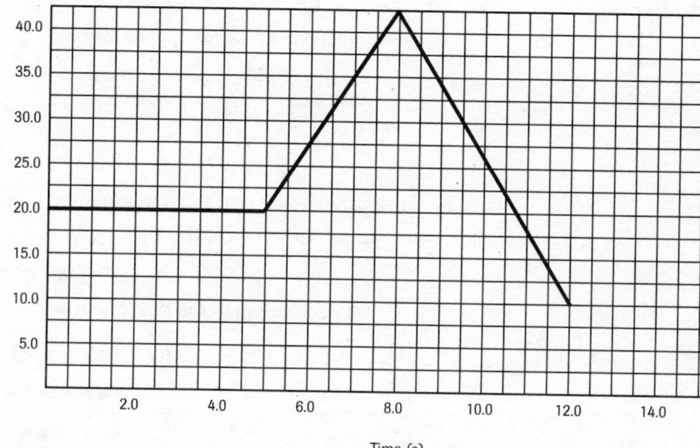

5. Describe the velocity and the acceleration of the object, using the graph you made for problem 4.
For the first 5.0 s, the velocity was constant. The object then increased velocity at a constant acceleration of 6.7 m/s^2 for 3.0 s. The object then decreased velocity at a constant acceleration of −7.5 m/s^2 for 4.0 s.

Name ______________

5 Chapter Assessment

Applying Concepts

Answer the following questions, using complete sentences.

1. In terms of graphing, distinguish between average velocity and instantaneous velocity.
   Average velocity is the slope of the line connecting any two points on a position-time graph. Instantaneous velocity is the slope of the tangent to the curve at a given time or instant of time.

2. When does an object have uniform motion?
   An object has uniform motion when it undergoes equal displacements in equal intervals of time.

3. On a position-time graph, compare the instantaneous velocities of an object when the tangent to the curve slopes upward to the right, when the tangent slopes downward to the right, and when the tangent is horizontal.
   If the tangent to the curve at a given point slopes upward to the right, the velocity is positive. If the tangent slopes downward to the right, the velocity is negative. At a point where the tangent is horizontal, the velocity is zero.

4. After making a delivery, a truck driver must maneuver the vehicle backward down a narrow ramp. The speed of the truck increases with distance down the ramp. Describe the truck's acceleration.
   Assuming backward is the negative direction, the truck's speed backward increases as it backs down the ramp, so its velocity increases in the negative direction. Therefore, its acceleration is negative.

5. How can you find the instantaneous acceleration of an object whose curve on the velocity-time graph is a straight line?
   The instantaneous acceleration is the slope of the straight line.

6. Suppose an object starts from rest. Explain how the displacement of the object, which has a constant acceleration, can be determined from a velocity-time graph.
   The displacement is the area under the curve on such a graph. The curve in this case is a straight line, yielding a triangular area.

7. How is the acceleration of an object in free-fall related to the acceleration due to gravity?
   For an object in free-fall, $a = g$.

Name ______________

5 Chapter Assessment

Answer the following questions, showing your calculations.

8. Using the graph you constructed for problem 4 in Understanding Concepts Part B, determine the object's displacement after 12.0 s.

   For 0.0–5.0 s

   $$d = d_0 + \frac{1}{2}(v_0 + v)t$$
   $$= 0.0\text{ m} + \frac{1}{2}(20.0\text{ m/s} + 20.0\text{ m/s})(5.0\text{ s})$$
   $$= 100\text{ m}$$

   For 5.0–8.0 s

   $$d = d_0 + \frac{1}{2}(v_0 + v)t$$
   $$= 100\text{ m} + \frac{1}{2}(20.0\text{ m/s} + 40.0\text{ m/s})(3.0\text{ s})$$
   $$= 190\text{ m}$$

   For 8.0–12.0 s

   $$d = d_0 + \frac{1}{2}(v_0 + v)t$$
   $$= 190\text{ m} + \frac{1}{2}(40.0\text{ m/s} + 10.0\text{ m/s})(4.0\text{ s})$$
   $$= 290\text{ m}$$

9. A toy rocket is shot straight up into the air with an initial speed of 45.0 m/s.

   a. How long does it take the rocket to reach its highest point?

   $$v = v_0 + gt \qquad t = \frac{v - v_0}{g} = \frac{0.0\text{ m/s} - 45.0\text{ m/s}}{-9.80\text{ m/s}^2} = 4.59\text{ s}$$

   b. How high does the rocket rise above the ground?

   $$v^2 = v_0^2 + 2g(d - d_0) \qquad d = \frac{v^2 - v_0^2}{2g} = \frac{(0.0\text{ m/s})^2 - (45.0\text{ m/s})^2}{2(-9.80\text{ m/s}^2)} = 103\text{ m}$$

Name ______________

5 Chapter Assessment

10. A squirrel drops an acorn from a tree branch that is 8.00 m from the ground.

a. How long is the acorn in the air?

$d = d_0 + \frac{1}{2}gt^2$ $\qquad t = \sqrt{\frac{2(d - d_0)}{g}}$

$= \sqrt{\frac{2(0 - 8.00\text{ m})}{-9.80\text{ m/s}^2}}$

$= \sqrt{1.63\text{ s}^2}$

$= 1.28\text{ s}$

b. What is the acorn's velocity when it reaches the ground?

$v^2 = v_0^2 + 2g(d - d_0)$

$v = \sqrt{v_0^2 + 2g(d - d_0)}$

$= \sqrt{(0.00\text{ m/s})^2 + 2(-9.80\text{ m/s})(0 - 8.00\text{ m})}$

$= -12.5\text{ m/s}$

11. Determine how long it takes a runner moving at 10.2 m/s on a circular track to go completely around the track once. The radius of the track is 25.0 m.

$d = d_0 + \bar{v}t \qquad t = \frac{d - d_0}{\bar{v}} = \frac{2\pi r - d_0}{\bar{v}}$

$= \frac{2\pi(25.0\text{ m}) - 0\text{ m}}{10.2\text{ m/s}}$

$= 15.4\text{ s}$

Date ______________ Period ______________ Name ______________

6 Chapter Assessment

Use with Chapter 6.

Forces

Understanding Concepts Part A

Write the letter of the choice that best completes the statement or answers the question.

__a__ **1.** According to Newton's _____ law, an object with no net force acting on it remains at rest or in motion with a constant velocity.

a. first **b.** second **c.** third

__b__ **2.** Losing speed as you ride your bike uphill demonstrates Newton's _____ law.

a. first **b.** second **c.** third

__c__ **3.** If you push against a wall, the wall pushes back against you with _____ force.

a. no **b.** less **c.** equal **d.** more

__b__ **4.** An object is in equilibrium if _____.

a. it has no weight
b. the net force on it is zero
c. it is accelerating
d. only one force is acting on it

__a__ **5.** The gravitational force exerted by a large body, such as Earth, is _____.

a. weight
b. mass
c. acceleration
d. inertial mass

__a__ **6.** Mass and weight are related by _____.

a. the force of gravity
b. newtons
c. friction
d. inertia

__a__ **7.** If the weight of a balloon is 3000 N and the lift force provided by the atmosphere is 3300 N, in which direction is the net force acting?

a. upward
b. downward
c. toward the east
d. toward the north

__c__ **8.** When the drag force on an object equals the force of gravity, the object attains _____.

a. acceleration
b. inertial mass
c. terminal velocity
d. maximum mass

__b__ **9.** The period of a simple pendulum depends upon _____.

a. the mass of the bob
b. the length of the pendulum
c. the amplitude of the swing
d. the stiffness of the pendulum

__a__ **10.** To produce mechanical resonance, the time between applied forces must equal the _____ of the object.

a. period
b. frequency
c. length
d. mass

Name ______________

6 Chapter Assessment

Understanding Concepts Part B

Answer the following questions, showing your calculations.

1. What force is required to accelerate a 6.0-kg bowling ball at +2.0 m/s²?

   $F = ma$
   $= (6.0\ \text{kg})(2.0\ \text{m/s}^2)$
   $= 12\ \text{kg·m/s}^2 = 12\ \text{N}$

2. What is the mass of a cat that weighs 30.0 N?

   $F_g = mg \qquad m = \frac{F_g}{g}$
   $= \frac{30.0\ \text{N}}{9.80\ \text{m/s}^2}$
   $= 3.06\ \text{kg}$

3. What is the tension in a rope that is supporting a 4.2-kg bucket?

   $F_T = F_g \qquad F_g = mg$
   $F_T = mg$
   $= (4.2\ \text{kg})(9.8\ \text{m/s}^2)$
   $= 41\ \text{kg·m/s}^2 = 41\ \text{N}$

4. A net force of +125 N acts on an object. Find the single force that will produce equilibrium.

   A force of −125 N will produce equilibrium.

5. The coefficient of sliding friction between a 78-kg box and a warehouse floor is 0.21. How much force is needed to keep the box moving at a constant velocity across the floor?

   $F_p = F_f \qquad F_N = F_g = mg \qquad F_f = \mu F_N = \mu mg$
   $F_p = \mu mg$
   $= (0.21)(78\ \text{kg})(9.8\ \text{m/s}^2)$
   $= 160\ \text{kg·m/s}^2 = 160\ \text{N}$

6. A 65-kg roller skater moves at a constant speed with a force of 75 N. What is the coefficient of friction between the skater and the floor of the roller rink?

   $F_p = F_f \qquad F_N = F_g = mg$
   $F_f = \mu F_N$
   $\mu = \frac{F_f}{F_N} = \frac{F_p}{mg}$
   $= \frac{75\ \text{N}}{(65\ \text{kg})(9.8\ \text{m/s}^2)}$
   $= 0.12$

Name ______________

6 Chapter Assessment

Applying Concepts

Answer the following questions, using complete sentences.

1. Explain the relationship between mass and weight on Earth. Would this relationship change on Mars? Give a reason for your answer.

   The weight of any object is equal to the product of the mass of the object and the acceleration due to gravity. The force of gravity on Mars is different from the force of gravity on Earth. Mass would not change, but weight would change. However, mass and weight would still be proportional.

2. An elevator is traveling from the lobby to the top of a building. As it slows to a stop on the top floor, what happens to your apparent weight?

   As the elevator slows, your acceleration is in the direction opposite to your velocity. The direction of the acceleration of the elevator is down. Thus the net force on you is downward. Your apparent weight is equal to an upward force equal to your weight plus the net force acting on you. In this case, the net force is downward, so your apparent weight would be $F_g - F_{net}$. Your apparent weight would decrease.

3. In the drawing below, use arrows to show the two horizontal and two vertical forces acting on the boat as it is pulled to the shore at a constant speed. Is there a net force on the boat?

   No, there is no net force on the boat because it has neither vertical nor horizontal acceleration.

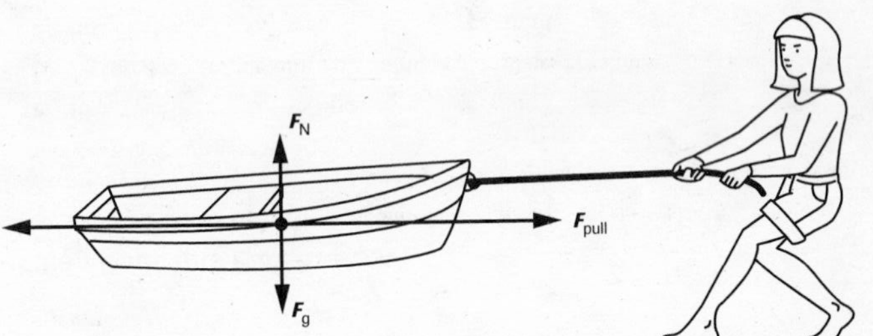

Name ____________

6 Chapter Assessment

4. Explain what is meant by an interaction pair. Use the boat in the drawing on page 25 to give an example.

   Interaction pairs are forces that act on different objects; they are equal in magnitude but opposite in direction. The drawing shows an interaction pair; the girl pulls on the boat with the same force that the boat pulls on her.

5. Suppose you pull on a rope tied to a large carton but you cannot move the carton. What forces are acting on your hand?

   They are the forces exerted by your arm muscles and the force exerted by the rope.

6. Describe the displacement, speed, and acceleration of a mass suspended on a vibrating spring as it passes through its equilibrium point.

   When the mass passes through its equilibrium point, its displacement and acceleration are zero and speed is at its maximum.

7. Cite an example of the electromagnetic interaction as a long-range force.

   The attraction or repulsion of the poles of magnets and the attraction or repulsion of electric charges are possible examples.

Name ____________

6 Chapter Assessment

Answer the following questions, showing your calculations.

8. An elevator with a mass of 1.10×10^3 kg accelerates upward at 0.45 m/s^2. What is the force acting on the elevator's support cable?

   $F_T = F_{net} + F_g = ma + mg$

   $F_T = m(a + g)$

   $= (1.10 \times 10^3 \text{ kg})(0.45 \text{ m/s}^2 + 9.8 \text{ m/s}^2)$

   $= 1.1 \times 10^4 \text{ kg·m/s}^2 = 1.1 \times 10^4 \text{ N}$

9. A rocket weighs 2.0×10^7 N. Its engines exert a force of $+25 \times 10^6$ N at liftoff.

   a. What is the mass of the rocket?

   $F_g = mg \qquad m = \frac{F_g}{g}$

   $= \frac{2.0 \times 10^7 \text{ N}}{9.8 \text{ m/s}^2} = \frac{2.0 \times 10^7 \text{ kg·m/s}^2}{9.8 \text{ m/s}^2}$

   $= 2.0 \times 10^6 \text{ kg}$

   b. What is its acceleration when it lifts off?

   $F_{thrust} = ma \qquad a = \frac{F_{thrust}}{m}$

   $= \frac{+25 \times 10^6 \text{ N}}{2.0 \times 10^6 \text{ kg}} = \frac{+25 \times 10^6 \text{ kg·m/s}^2}{2.0 \times 10^6 \text{ kg}}$

   $= 13 \text{ m/s}^2$

   c. The average acceleration of the rocket during its 7.0-min launch is 10.0 m/s^2. What velocity does it reach?

   $v_f = v_i + at$

   $= 0.0 \text{ m/s} + (10.0 \text{ m/s}^2)(7.0 \text{ min})(60 \text{ s/min})$

   $= 4200 \text{ m/s}$

Name ______________

6 Chapter Assessment

10. A 47-N box is pulled along a frictionless horizontal surface by a 25-N weight hanging from a cord on a frictionless pulley.

a. What is the acceleration of the box and the weight?

$F = F_{1g} = m_1 g = 25\ \text{N}$

$F_{1g} = m_1 g \qquad m_1 = \frac{F_{1g}}{g} = \frac{25\ \text{N}}{9.8\ \text{m/s}^2} = \frac{25\ \text{kg·m/s}^2}{9.8\ \text{m/s}^2} = 2.6\ \text{kg}$

$F_{2g} = m_2 g \qquad m_2 = \frac{F_{2g}}{g} = \frac{47\ \text{N}}{9.8\ \text{m/s}^2} = \frac{47\ \text{kg·m/s}^2}{9.8\ \text{m/s}^2} = 4.8\ \text{kg}$

$F = ma \qquad a = \frac{F}{m} = \frac{F}{(m_1 + m_2)} = \frac{25\ \text{N}}{(2.6\ \text{kg} + 4.8\ \text{kg})} = \frac{25\ \text{kg·m/s}^2}{7.4\ \text{kg}} = 3.4\ \text{m/s}^2$

b. What force is exerted on the cord?

$F_{cord} = m_2 a$

$= (2.6\ \text{kg})(3.4\ \text{m/s}^2)$

$= 8.8\ \text{kg·m/s}^2 = 8.8\ \text{N}$

Date ______________ Period ______________ Name ______________

7 Chapter Assessment

Use with Chapter 7.

Forces and Motion in Two Dimensions

Understanding Concepts Part A

Write the letter of the choice that best completes the statement or answers the question.

__c__ **1.** The equilibrant force is ____ the resultant.

- **a.** greater than and in the same direction as
- **b.** less than but opposite in direction to
- **c.** equal in magnitude but opposite in direction to
- **d.** equal in magnitude and in the same direction as

__d__ **2.** As the angle of an inclined plane increases, the parallel component of the weight force ____ and the perpendicular component of the weight force ____.

- **a.** decreases, decreases
- **b.** decreases, increases
- **c.** increases, increases
- **d.** increases, decreases

__d__ **3.** The horizontal acceleration of a projectile ____ as its position changes.

- **a.** increases
- **b.** decreases
- **c.** is constant
- **d.** is zero

__c__ **4.** The initial horizontal velocity of a projectile is ____ its final horizontal velocity.

a. greater than **b.** less than **c.** equal to

__c__ **5.** The rising and falling times of a projectile are equal if the launching position is ____ the landing position.

a. above **b.** below **c.** at the same height as

__c__ **6.** For a fast ball to pass the height of a batter's chest, the pitcher must aim the ball ____.

- **a.** exactly at the height of the batter's chest
- **b.** slightly below the height of the batter's chest
- **c.** just above the height of the batter's chest

__c__ **7.** An object in circular motion travels a distance of ____ during its period.

- **a.** r
- **b.** $4\pi r^2$
- **c.** $2\pi r$
- **d.** v^2/r

__c__ **8.** To start or stop rotation, the force applied to an object must ____.

- **a.** act toward the axis of rotation of the object
- **b.** be greater than the object's weight
- **c.** have a component that is perpendicular to the lever arm
- **d.** act outward from the axis of rotation of the object

Name ____________

7 Chapter Assessment

Understanding Concepts Part B

Answer the following questions, showing your calculations.

1. A crate weighing 823 N rests on a plank that makes a 25.0° angle with the ground. Find the components of the crate's weight force parallel and perpendicular to the plank.

$F_{gx} = -F \sin\theta$

$= -(823\text{ N})(0.423)$

$= -348\text{ N}$

$F_{gy} = -F_g \cos\theta$

$= -(823\text{ N})(0.906)$

$= -746\text{ N}$

2. A soccer player kicks a ball into the air at an angle of 36.0° above the horizontal. The initial velocity of the ball is +30.0 m/s. How long is the soccer ball in the air?

$v_{y0} = v_0 \sin\theta$

$= (30.0\text{ m/s})(0.588)$

$= 17.6\text{ m/s}$

$t = \frac{2v_{y0}}{g}$

$= \frac{(2)(17.6\text{ m/s})}{9.80\text{ m/s}^2}$

$= 3.59\text{ s}$

3. What is the horizontal distance traveled by the soccer ball in problem 2?

$v_{x0} = v_0 \cos\theta$

$= (30.0\text{ m/s})(0.809)$

$= 24.3\text{ m/s}$

$R = v_{x0}t$

$= (24.3\text{ m/s})(3.59\text{ s})$

$= 87.2\text{ m}$

Name ____________

7 Chapter Assessment

4. What is the maximum height reached by the soccer ball in problem 2?

$t = \frac{v_{y0}}{g}$

$= \frac{17.6\text{ m/s}}{9.80\text{ m/s}^2}$

$= 1.80\text{ s}$

$y_{max} = v_{y0}t - \frac{1}{2}gt^2$

$= (17.6\text{ m/s})(1.80\text{ s}) - \frac{1}{2}(9.80\text{ m/s}^2)(1.80\text{ s})^2$

$= 15.8\text{ m}$

5. A runner moving at a speed of 5.6 m/s rounds a curved track with a 65 m-radius. What is the runner's centripetal acceleration?

$a_c = \frac{v^2}{r}$

$= \frac{(5.6\text{ m/s})^2}{65\text{ m}}$

$= 0.48\text{ m/s}^2$

6. A person with a mass of 75 kg sits at a distance of 1.5 m from the pivot point on a 4.0-m seesaw. Where would a person with a mass of 65 kg have to sit to balance the seesaw?

$m_1gd_1 = m_2gd_2$

$d_2 = \frac{m_1d_1}{m_2}$

$= \frac{(75\text{ kg})(1.5\text{ m})}{65\text{ kg}}$

$= 1.7\text{ m}$

Name ______________

7 Chapter Assessment

Applying Concepts

Answer the following questions, using complete sentences.

1. What is the relationship between the components of the weight of an object and the angle of an inclined plane on which the object rests?
The parallel component of the weight force is proportional to the sine of the angle that the plane makes with the horizontal. The perpendicular component of the weight force is proportional to the cosine that the angle makes with the horizontal.

2. What is the equilibrant of the perpendicular component of the weight force of a crate resting on an incline?
It is the normal force.

3. What is the equilibrant of the parallel component of the weight force of a crate resting on an incline?
It is the force of static friction.

4. Compare the distance a ball falls during the first second after it is dropped with the distance it falls during the second second.
The ball accelerates as it falls. Each second its velocity increases, so it falls a greater distance during the second second.

5. If a ball is thrown down instead of being dropped from rest, is the average velocity for its downward motion different? Would its being thrown affect the time required to fall to the ground? Give reasons for your answers.
The average velocity would be greater because the initial velocity was not zero. The time required for the fall would decrease because of the greater velocity.

6. Two people are on a carnival ride that uses centripetal and frictional forces to hold its riders in place inside a rotating drum. How do the velocity, acceleration, and force acting on the people differ if one person has twice the mass of the other?
The velocity and the acceleration of the two riders are the same. The static friction force required to hold the more massive person in place is greater than that required to hold the other person.

7. On a game show, contestants spin a large wheel to determine the prize associated with correct answers. How should a contestant apply force to spin the wheel as rapidly as possible?
A contestant should apply as much force as possible tangential to the rim of the wheel.

Name ______________

7 Chapter Assessment

Answer the following questions, showing your calculations.

8. A 125-N sign is supported by a lightweight pole and cable as shown in the diagram. What is the tension in the cable?

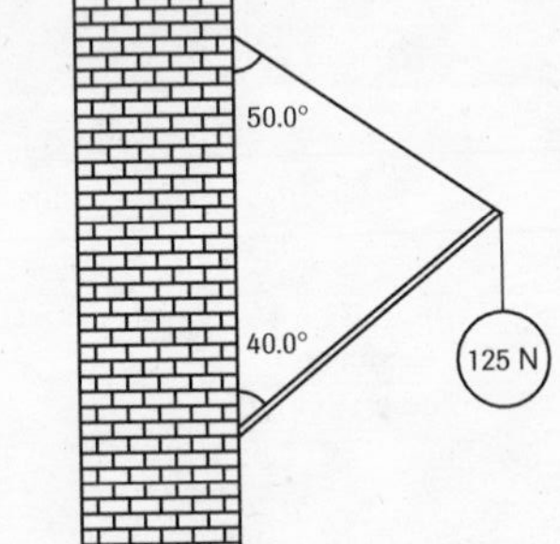

$F_{yT} - F_g = 0$　　$F_T \cos\theta = F_g$　　$\theta = 50.0°$

$$F_T = \frac{F_g}{\cos\theta} = \frac{125\ \text{N}}{0.643} = 194\ \text{N}$$

9. A 15-kg suitcase begins to slide down a luggage chute that makes an angle of 30.0° with the horizontal. The coefficient of kinetic friction for the suitcase and shoot is 0.45. What is the acceleration of the suitcase?

$F_x = F_{xg} - \mu F_N = F_{xg} - \mu(F_{yg})$

$F_x = F_g \sin\theta - \mu(F_g \cos\theta)$

$ma_x = mg \sin\theta - \mu(mg \cos\theta)$

$a_x = g(\sin\theta - \mu\cos\theta)$

$= 9.80\ \text{m/s}^2\ (0.500 - (0.45)(0.866))$

$= 9.80\ \text{m/s}^2\ (0.110)$

$= 1.1\ \text{m/s}^2$ (down the chute)

Name ______________

7 Chapter Assessment

10. A coin rolls along the top of a 1.33 m-high desk with a constant velocity. It reaches the edge of the desk and hits the ground +0.25 m from the edge of the desk. What was the velocity of the coin as it rolled across the desk?

$$y = y_0 + v_{y0}t - \tfrac{1}{2}gt^2$$

$$t^2 = \frac{-2y}{g}$$

$$t = \sqrt{\frac{-2y}{g}}$$

$$= \sqrt{\frac{(-2)(-1.33\text{ m})}{9.8\text{ m/s}^2}}$$

$$= 0.52\text{ s}$$

$$R = v_{x0}t;\; v_{x0} = \frac{R}{t}$$

$$= \frac{0.25\text{ m}}{0.52\text{ s}}$$

$$= 0.48\text{ m/s}$$

11. A 0.050-kg disk attached to the end of a 0.150-m wire revolves uniformly on a flat, frictionless surface.

a. If the disk makes three complete revolutions per second, what is the force exerted by the wire on the object?

$$F_c = ma_c = \frac{4\pi^2 mr}{T^2}$$

$$= \frac{(4)\,(3.14)^2\,(0.050\text{ kg})\,(0.150\text{ m})}{((1.00\text{ s})/3)^2}$$

$$= 2.7\text{ N}$$

b. What is the speed of the disk?

$$v = \frac{d}{t} = \frac{2\pi r}{T}$$

$$= \frac{(2)(3.14)(0.15\text{ m})}{((1.00\text{ s})/3)}$$

$$= 2.8\text{ m/s}$$

Date ______________ Period ______________ Name ______________

8 Chapter Assessment

Use with Chapter 8.

Universal Gravitation

Understanding Concepts Part A

Write the letter of the choice that best completes each statement.

__a__ **1.** During its orbital period, as a planet moves closer to the sun, the orbital velocity of the planet _____.

a. increases **b.** decreases **c.** remains the same

__b__ **2.** According to Newton's law of universal gravitation, the force of attraction between any two masses is directly related to the _____.

a. distance between the masses
b. product of the two masses
c. velocity of the two masses
d. sum of the two masses

__b__ **3.** As the distance between two bodies increases, the force of attraction between the bodies _____.

a. increases **b.** decreases **c.** remains the same

__a__ **4.** Astronauts in an orbiting space shuttle experience a sensation of weightlessness because _____.

a. the space shuttle is falling freely toward Earth
b. the space shuttle is not affected by Earth's gravity
c. the mass of the space shuttle decreases as the distance from Earth increases
d. the space shuttle is moving away from Earth

__c__ **5.** Anything that has mass is surrounded by a _____.

a. satellite in orbit
b. magnetic field
c. gravitational field
d. black hole

__b__ **6.** The force of gravity exerts a _____ on an orbiting satellite.

a. balanced force
b. centripetal force
c. tangential force
d. All these are true.

__b__ **7.** The pair of spheres that experiences the greatest force of attraction is _____.

a. A and B
b. B and C
c. A and C

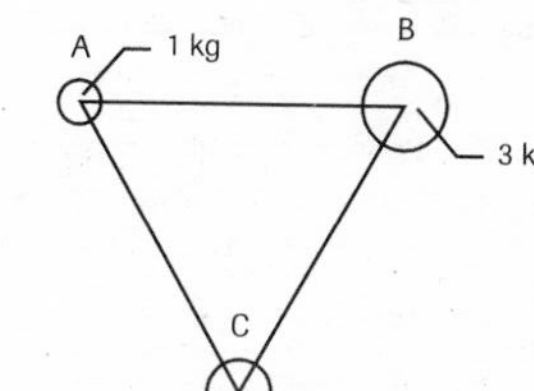

Name ____________

8 Chapter Assessment

Understanding Concepts Part B

Answer the following questions, showing your calculations.

1. Which of the pairs of masses below will have the greatest force of attraction between the spheres?

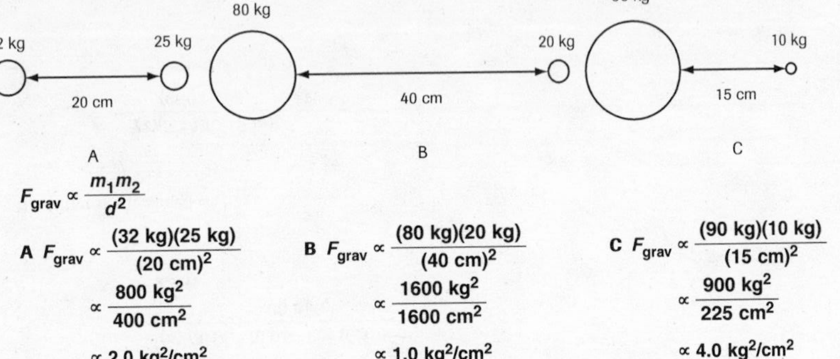

$F_{grav} \propto \frac{m_1 m_2}{d^2}$

A $F_{grav} \propto \frac{(32\ kg)(25\ kg)}{(20\ cm)^2} \propto \frac{800\ kg^2}{400\ cm^2} \propto 2.0\ kg^2/cm^2$

B $F_{grav} \propto \frac{(80\ kg)(20\ kg)}{(40\ cm)^2} \propto \frac{1600\ kg^2}{1600\ cm^2} \propto 1.0\ kg^2/cm^2$

C $F_{grav} \propto \frac{(90\ kg)(10\ kg)}{(15\ cm)^2} \propto \frac{900\ kg^2}{225\ cm^2} \propto 4.0\ kg^2/cm^2$

The force of attraction will be the greatest between the spheres in set C.

2. Two spheres, each having a mass of 20.0 kg, are positioned so that their centers are 8.00 m apart. What is the gravitational force between the spheres?

$F = G\frac{m_1 m_2}{d^2}$

$= \frac{(6.67 \times 10^{-11}\ N{\cdot}m^2/kg^2)(2.00 \times 10^1\ kg)(2.00 \times 10^1\ kg)}{(8.0\ m)^2}$

$= 4.17 \times 10^{-10}\ N$

3. What will the force be if the spheres described in problem 2 are positioned with their centers 4.00 m apart?

$F = G\frac{m_1 m_2}{d^2}$

$= \frac{(6.67 \times 10^{-11}\ N{\cdot}m^2/kg^2)(2.00 \times 10^1\ kg)(2.00 \times 10^1\ kg)}{(4.0\ m)^2}$

$= 1.67 \times 10^{-9}\ N$

4. If the mass of one of the spheres described in problem 2 were doubled, how far apart would the spheres have to be to maintain the same gravitational force between them?

$d = \sqrt{\frac{G m_1 m_2}{F}} = \sqrt{\frac{(6.67 \times 10^{-11}\ N{\cdot}m^2/kg^2)(4.00 \times 10^1\ kg)(2.00 \times 10^1\ kg)}{(4.17 \times 10^{-10}\ N)}}$

$= \sqrt{1.28 \times 10^2\ m^2}$

$= 11.3\ m$

Name ____________

8 Chapter Assessment

Applying Concepts

Answer the following questions, using complete sentences.

1. Explain why Kepler was able to use Tycho Brahe's data about the positions of stars and planets to develop his laws of planetary motion, while Brahe was unable to use the same data successfully.
Brahe believed in an Earth-centered universe. In formulating his laws of planetary motion, Kepler applied Brahe's data to the motions of planets in a sun-centered system.

2. Earth is closer to the sun in December than it is in July. What happens to the orbital speed of the planet between July and December? Explain your answer.
The orbital speed of Earth increases between July and December. During this period, Earth is moving closer to the sun, and the closer a planet is to the sun, the faster the planet moves in its orbit.

3. What would happen to the magnitude of the gravitational force between two bodies if:
   a. the mass of one of the bodies were doubled?
   The gravitational force between them would be doubled.
   b. the distance between the two bodies were doubled?
   The gravitational force between them would be one-fourth as great.

4. What information do you need to find the period of a planet using Kepler's third law?
You need to know the period of another planet and the orbital radii of both planets.

5. The mass of Jupiter is approximately 318 times that of Earth. Yet the surface gravity of Jupiter is less than three times the surface gravity of Earth. How do you account for this apparent discrepancy?
The surface gravity of each planet is inversely related to the square of the radius of the planet. Jupiter's radius is much greater (almost 11 times) than Earth's radius.

6. How does an artificial satellite remain in orbit at a constant distance from Earth's surface?
The satellite moves with uniform circular motion so that the curvature of Earth's surface exactly matches the curvature of the trajectory of the satellite. Earth's surface "falls away" from the satellite at the same rate that the satellite falls toward Earth.

7. How does Einstein's general theory of relativity account for the blackness of black holes in the universe?
According to Einstein's theory, light is deflected by the mass of a body. If an object is massive enough, light leaving the object will be bent back toward it. If no light ever escapes the object, the object appears to be a black hole.

Name ____________

8 Chapter Assessment

Answer the following questions, showing your calculations.

8. The distance between Earth and the sun is often expressed as 1 astronomical unit (AU). Using this unit, find the distance between the sun and Mars, which has a period of approximately 686 Earth days.

$$\left(\frac{T_M}{T_E}\right)^2 = \left(\frac{r_M}{r_E}\right)^3 \qquad r_M = r_E\left(\frac{T_M^2}{T_E^2}\right)^{\frac{1}{3}}$$

$$r_M = 1\ \text{AU}\left(\frac{(686\ \text{d})^2}{(365\ \text{d})^2}\right)^{\frac{1}{3}} = 1\ \text{AU}(3.53)^{\frac{1}{3}} = 1.52\ \text{AU}$$

9. The mean distance between the center of Earth and the center of the moon is 3.84×10^8 m, and the moon has an orbital period of 27.3 days. Find the distance from Earth of an artificial satellite that has an orbital period of 9.1 days.

$$\left(\frac{T_s}{T_m}\right)^2 = \left(\frac{r_s}{r_m}\right)^3 \qquad r_s = r_m\left(\frac{T_s^2}{T_m^2}\right)^{\frac{1}{3}} \qquad r_s = 3.84 \times 10^8\ \text{m}\left(\frac{(9.1\ \text{d})^2}{(27.3\ \text{d})^2}\right)^{\frac{1}{3}}$$

$$= 3.84 \times 10^8\ \text{m}\ (0.11)^{\frac{1}{3}}$$

$$= 1.84 \times 10^8\ \text{m}$$

10. The gravitational force between two spheres is 2.50×10^{-8} N. Their centers are 105 cm apart. The smaller sphere has a mass of 8.2 kg. Find the mass of the larger sphere.

$$F = \frac{G m_1 m_2}{d^2} \qquad m_2 = \frac{Fd^2}{Gm_1}$$

$$= \frac{(2.50 \times 10^{-8}\ \text{N})(1.05\ \text{m})^2}{(6.67 \times 10^{-11}\ \text{N·m}^2/\text{kg}^2)(8.2\ \text{kg})}$$

$$= 50\ \text{kg}$$

11. A body orbits the sun at a distance ten times the mean distance of Earth's orbit from the sun. The sun's mass is 1.99×10^{30} kg, and its distance from Earth is 1.50×10^{11} m.

a. Find the period of the body in years.

$$\left(\frac{T_x}{T_E}\right)^2 = \left(\frac{r_x}{r_E}\right)^3 \qquad T_x = T_E\sqrt{\frac{r_x^3}{r_E^3}} = \sqrt{\frac{T_E\,(10r_E)^3}{r_E^3}}$$

$$= (1\ \text{year})\sqrt{\frac{10^3}{1^3}}$$

$$= 32\ \text{years}$$

b. Determine the speed of the body.

$$v = \sqrt{\frac{Gm_s}{r}} = \sqrt{\frac{(6.67 \times 10^{-11}\ \text{N·m}^2/\text{kg})(1.99 \times 10^{30}\ \text{kg})}{(1.50 \times 10^{12}\ \text{m})}}$$

$$= 9.41 \times 10^3\ \text{m/s}$$

Date ____________ Period ____________ Name ____________

9 Chapter Assessment

Use with Chapter 9.

Momentum and Its Conservation

Understanding Concepts Part A

Write the letter of the choice that best completes the statement or answers the question.

__b__ **1.** The linear momentum of an object can be calculated by multiplying the mass of the object by its _____.

a. acceleration **c.** impulse
b. velocity **d.** time

__a__ **2.** The greatest change in momentum will be produced by a _____.

a. large force acting over a long time
b. small force acting over a short time
c. large force acting over a short time

__b__ **3.** Impulse can be represented by _____.

a. $\Delta v/\Delta t$ **c.** mv
b. $F\Delta t$ **d.** m/v

__a__ **4.** When a golf club hits a golf ball, the change in momentum of the ball is _____ the change in momentum of the club.

a. equal to **b.** greater than **c.** less than

__c__ **5.** A system is closed if _____.

a. no net external force acts on it
b. the momentum of each object in the system remains constant
c. the system does not gain or lose mass
d. objects can enter, but not leave, the system

__c__ **6.** An internal force _____ the total momentum of a closed system.

a. increases **b.** decreases **c.** does not change

__b__ **7.** A person is standing on roller blades and is holding a heavy medicine ball. If he throws the medicine ball horizontally to the right, what will be his resulting motion?

a. to the right **c.** backward
b. to the left **d.** no motion

__a__ **8.** Two moving objects collide and move on paths that are 120° apart. The total momentum of the objects after the collision is _____ the total momentum before the collision.

a. equal to **b.** greater than **c.** less than

Name ____________

9 Chapter Assessment

Understanding Concepts Part B

Answer the following questions, showing your calculations.

1. What is the momentum of a 145-g baseball traveling at +40.0 m/s?

$p = mv$

$= (0.145\ \text{kg})(40.0\ \text{m/s})$

$= 5.80\ \text{kg·m/s}$

2. What impulse is needed to stop a 45-g mass traveling at a velocity of –42 m/s?

$F\Delta t = m\Delta v$

$= (0.045\ \text{kg})(42\ \text{m/s})$

$= 1.9\ \text{N·s}$

3. A force with a magnitude of 540 N is used to stop an object with a mass of 65 kg moving at a velocity of +175 m/s. How long will it take to bring the object to a full stop?

$F\Delta t = m\Delta v \qquad \Delta t = \frac{m\Delta v}{F}$

$= \frac{m(v_2 - v_1)}{F}$

$= \frac{(65\ \text{kg})(0\ \text{m/s} - 175\ \text{m/s})}{-540\ \text{kg·m/s}^2}$

$= 21\ \text{s}$

4. In hitting a stationary hockey puck having a mass of 180 g, a hockey player gives the puck an impulse of 6.0 N·s. At what speed will the puck move toward the goal?

$F\Delta t = m\Delta v \qquad \Delta v = \frac{F\Delta t}{m}$

$v_2 - 0 = \Delta v = \frac{(6.0\ \text{N·s})}{0.18\ \text{kg}} = \frac{(6.0\ \text{kg·m/s})}{0.18\ \text{kg}}$

$v_2 = 33\ \text{m/s}$

Name ____________

9 Chapter Assessment

5. A metal sphere with a mass of 80.0 g rolls along a frictionless surface at 20.0 m/s and strikes a stationary sphere having a mass of 200.0 g. The first sphere stops completely. At what speed does the second sphere move away from the point of impact?

$p_{A1} + p_{B1} = p_{A2} + p_{B2}$

$p_{A1} + 0 = 0 + p_{B2}$

$p_{A1} = p_{B2}$

$m_A v_{A1} = m_B v_{B2} \qquad v_{B2} = \frac{m_A v_{A1}}{m_B}$

$= \frac{(0.0800\ \text{kg})(20.0\ \text{m/s})}{0.2000\ \text{kg}}$

$= 8.00\ \text{m/s}$

6. A snowball with a mass of 85 g hits a snowman's top hat and sticks to it. The hat and the snowball, with a combined mass of 220 g, fall off together at 8.0 m/s. How fast was the snowball moving at the moment of impact?

$p_{A1} + p_{B1} = p_{A2+B2}$

$p_{A1} + 0 = p_{A2+B2}$

$m_A v_{A1} = (m_A + m_B)v_{A2+B2} \qquad v_{A1} = \frac{(m_A + m_B)v_{A2+B2}}{m_A}$

$= \frac{(0.22\ \text{kg})(8.0\ \text{m/s})}{0.085\ \text{kg}}$

$= 21\ \text{m/s}$

Name ______________

9 Chapter Assessment

Applying Concepts

Answer the following questions, using complete sentences.

1. Explain how a motorcycle can have the same linear momentum as an automobile.
   Because linear momentum is the product of an object's mass and velocity, the less massive motorcycle must have proportionately greater velocity to have the same linear momentum as an automobile.

2. To bunt a baseball effectively, at the instant the ball strikes the bat, the batter moves the bat in the same direction as the moving baseball. What effect does this action have? Why?
   It reduces the velocity at which the ball rebounds from the bat. When the bat moves in the same direction as the moving ball, the two are in contact for less time than when the bat moves toward the ball. Because the two are in contact for less time, the impulse on the ball is reduced, and its change in momentum, and therefore its change in velocity, is reduced. The smaller change in velocity indicates that the ball rebounds from a bunt at less velocity than from a normal swing.

3. In the sport of curling, players slide 19-kg masses called stones along the surface of the ice toward a target. If a stone traveling 3 m/s strikes a stationary stone directly, the first stone will stop moving. Using the concept of conservation of momentum, describe what happens to the second stone. Assume there is no friction.
   Because the two stones are an isolated, closed system, momentum is conserved. Therefore, the second stone will move in the same direction and at the same speed as the first.

4. Why does a fire hose recoil when the water is turned on?
   Before the water is turned on, the momentum of the hose-and-water system is zero. After the water is turned on, the water gains momentum as it is pushed forward from the hose. Because the hose and water form an isolated, closed system, momentum is conserved. For the momentum of the system to remain zero, the hose gains an equal magnitude of momentum in the opposite direction. The backward momentum of the hose gives it a backward velocity, or recoil.

5. Suppose you were an astronaut drifting in space several meters from your spacecraft. The only thing you have with you is a sack filled with moon rocks. How could you return to your ship?
   While holding the rocks, you and the rocks form an isolated, closed system, with an initial momentum of zero. Because the momentum of such a system is conserved, at a later time the momentum of the system has to be zero. If you give the rocks momentum by throwing them away from the ship, you will gain momentum in the opposite direction, which means you will move toward the ship.

Name ______________

9 Chapter Assessment

Answer the following questions, showing your calculations.

6. A ball with a mass of 12 g moving at +15.0 m/s collides with a second ball with a mass of 36 g moving at +5.0 m/s. After the collision, the 12-g ball moves at +6.0 m/s. What is the change in momentum of the 36-g ball?

$$p_{A1} + p_{B1} = p_{A2} + p_{B2}$$

$$m_A v_{A1} + m_B v_{B1} = m_A v_{A2} + m_B v_{B2}$$

$$v_{B2} = \frac{m_A v_{A1} + m_B v_{B1} - m_A v_{A2}}{m_B}$$

$$= \frac{(0.012\ \text{kg})(15.0\ \text{m/s}) + (0.036\ \text{kg})(5.0\ \text{m/s}) - (0.012\ \text{kg})(6.0\ \text{m/s})}{0.036\ \text{kg}}$$

$$= +8.0\ \text{m/s}$$

$$\Delta p_B = p_{B2} - p_{B1} = m_B v_{B2} - m_B v_{B1}$$

$$= m_B(v_{B2} - v_{B1})$$

$$= (0.036\ \text{kg})(8.0\ \text{m/s} - 5.0\ \text{m/s})$$

$$= +0.11\ \text{kg}\cdot\text{m/s}$$

7. A 24.0-kg dog running at a speed of 3.0 m/s jumps onto a stationary skateboard that has a mass of 3.6 kg. How long will it take an average force with a magnitude 9.0 N to stop the skateboard and dog?

$$p_{A1} + p_{B1} = p_{A2+B2}$$

$$p_{A1} + 0 = p_{A2+B2}$$

$$m_A v_{A1} = (m_A + m_B)v_{A2+B2}$$

$$v_{A2+B2} = \frac{m_A v_{A1}}{(m_B + m_A)}$$

$$= \frac{(24.0\ \text{kg})(3.0\ \text{m/s})}{27.6\ \text{kg}}$$

$$= 2.6\ \text{m/s}$$

$$F\Delta t = m\Delta v$$

$$\Delta t = \frac{m\Delta v}{F}$$

$$= \frac{m(v_2 - v_1)}{F}$$

$$= \frac{(27.6\ \text{kg})(0\ \text{m/s} - 2.6\ \text{m/s})}{-9.0\ \text{kg}\cdot\text{m/s}^2}$$

$$= 8.0\ \text{s}$$

Name ______________

9 Chapter Assessment

8. A sphere of mass 5.00 kg moving at 4.00 m/s collides with an identical sphere that is at rest. The first sphere moves off at an angle of 60.0° to the left of its original path, and the second sphere moves off in a direction 90.0° to the right of the first sphere's final path. What are the speeds of the two spheres as they separate? Assume frictionless conditions.

$p_1 = p_{A1} + p_{B1} = p_{A2} + p_{B2} = p_2$

$p_{A1} = m_A v_{A1} = (5.00\text{ kg})(4.00\text{ m/s}) = 20.0\text{ kg·m/s}$

$p_{B1} = m_B v_{B1} = (5.00\text{ kg})(0.00\text{ m/s}) = 0.0\text{ kg·m/s}$

$p_1 = p_{A1} + p_{B1} = 20.0\text{ kg·m/s} = p_2$

$p_{A2} = p_2 \cos 60.0° = (20.0\text{ kg·m/s})(0.500) = 10.0\text{ kg·m/s}$

$p_{B2} = p_2 \sin 60.0° = (20.0\text{ kg·m/s})(0.866) = 17.3\text{ kg·m/s}$

$p_{A2} = m_A v_{A2}$

$v_{A2} = \frac{p_{A2}}{m_A} = \frac{10.0\text{ kg·m/s}}{5.00\text{ kg}} = 2.00\text{ m/s}$

$p_{B2} = m_B v_{B2}$

$v_{B2} = \frac{p_{B2}}{m_B} = \frac{17.3\text{ kg·m/s}}{5.00\text{ kg}} = 3.46\text{ m/s}$

Date ______________ Period ______________ Name ______________

10 Chapter Assessment

Use with Chapter 10.

Energy, Work, and Simple Machines

Understanding Concepts Part A

Write the letter of the choice that best completes the statement or answers the question.

b 1. Any object that has energy has the ability to ____.
- a. burn
- b. produce a change
- c. fall

b 2. If the environment does work on a system, ____.
- a. the environment warms
- b. the energy of the system increases
- c. the energy of the system decreases
- d. the quantity of work done on the system has a negative value

c 3. When a force is exerted on an object, work is done only if the object ____.
- a. is heavy
- b. remains stationary
- c. moves
- d. has no momentum

b 4. In which of the following situations is no work done on a football?
- a. picking up the football
- b. carrying the football down the field
- c. dropping the football

a 5. In which of the following situations is work done on the football by a person?
- a. picking up the football
- b. carrying the football down the field
- c. dropping the football

c 6. In which of the following situations is work done on the football by gravity?
- a. picking up the football
- b. carrying the football down the field
- c. dropping the football

Write the term that correctly completes each statement.

7. One definition of **power** is "work done per unit time."
8. A machine with a mechanical advantage greater than 1 increases **effort force**.
9. For an ideal machine, efficiency is always **100** percent.
10. If the mechanical advantage of a machine is less than 1, effort force is **greater** than resistance force.
11. A wedge used to split wood is a **simple** machine.
12. A pair of gears make up a **compound** machine.

Name ______________

10 Chapter Assessment

Understanding Concepts Part B

Answer the following questions, showing your calculations.

1. How much work is done if you raise a 6.0-N weight 1.5 m above the ground?

   $W = Fd = (6.0\ \text{N})(1.5\ \text{m}) = 9.0\ \text{N·m} = 9.0\ \text{J}$

2. Using an ideal machine, a worker exerts an effort force of 5.0 N to lift a 12.0-N weight a distance of 3.0 m. How far does the effort force move?

   $F_e d_e = F_r d_r \quad d_e = \frac{F_r d_r}{F_e} = \frac{(12.0\ \text{N})(3.0\ \text{m})}{(5.0\ \text{N})} = 7.2\ \text{m}$

3. An effort force of 200.0 N is applied to an ideal machine to move a 750.0-N resistance a distance of 300.0 cm. What is the mechanical advantage of the machine?

   $MA = \frac{F_r}{F_e} = \frac{750.0\ \text{N}}{200.0\ \text{N}} = 3.750$

4. How much power is developed by an electric motor that moves a 500-N load a distance of 20 m in 10 s?

   $P = \frac{W}{t} = \frac{Fd}{t} = \frac{(500\ \text{N})(20\ \text{m})}{(10\ \text{s})} = 1000\ (\text{N·m})/\text{s} = 1000\ \text{W}$

5. What is the efficiency of a machine that requires a work input of 190 J to achieve a work output of 160 J?

   $\text{efficiency} = \frac{W_o}{W_i} \times 100\% = \frac{160\ \text{J}}{190\ \text{J}} \times 100\% = 84\%$

6. How much power is generated by a machine in lifting 250 kg a distance of 150 m in 30.0 s?

   $P = \frac{W}{t} = \frac{Fd}{t} = \frac{mgd}{t} = \frac{(250\ \text{kg})(9.80\ \text{m/s}^2)(150\ \text{m})}{(30.0\ \text{s})} = 1.2 \times 10^4\ (\text{N·m})/\text{s} = 1.2 \times 10^4\ \text{J}$

Name ______________

10 Chapter Assessment

Applying Concepts

Answer the following questions, using complete sentences.

1. Two students are moving 80-N cartons of books from the floor onto a platform. One student moves 12 cartons in 7 minutes. The other student moves the same number of cartons in 5 minutes. Which student does more work? Explain your answer.

   Each student does the same amount of work. Each exerts the same amount of force over the same distance.

2. What type of simple machine is the handle of a pencil sharpener? How does it make work easier?

   The handle is a wheel and axle. Force applied at the perimeter of the wheel is transferred to the axle at the center of the system, where it is multiplied and used to do work.

3. If a machine is used to increase force, what factor is sacrificed? Cite an example.

   Effort distance is sacrificed. Examples may vary, but should be machines in which a small effort force acts over a large distance to exert a large resistance force over a small distance.

4. Distinguish between work and power.

   Work is the transfer of energy by mechanical means. Power is the rate at which that energy is transferred. Power involves time; work does not.

5. Explain the following: When a screwdriver is used to drive a screw, the diameter of its handle is more important than its length, but when used to pry open a stuck window, its length is more important than the diameter of its handle.

   When used to drive a screw, a screwdriver is a wheel and axle; the larger the ratio of the diameter of the handle to the shaft, the greater the *IMA* of the machine. When used to pry open a window, the screwdriver is a lever, in which the edge of the windowsill is the fulcrum. The longer the effort arm of the lever, the greater its *IMA*.

6. Use mechanical advantage to explain what happens when you shift the gears of a multispeed bike.

   The gears in a bike are a type of wheel-and-axle machine in which the *MA* is the ratio of the effort gear attached to the pedals and the resistance gear attached to the rear wheel. Shifting gears changes this gear ratio, thus changing the *MA* of the wheel and axle.

Name ______________

10 Chapter Assessment

Answer the following questions, showing your calculations.

7. An adult and a child exert a total force of 930 N in pushing a car 15 m down their driveway. The adult exerts twice as much force as the child. How much work does each person do?

Total force, $F = 930$ N
Force exerted by adult,
$F = (930\ \text{N})(\frac{2}{3}) = 620$ N
Work done by adult,
$W = Fd$
$= (620\ \text{N})(15\ \text{m}) = 9300\ \text{N}\cdot\text{m}$
$= 9300$ J

Force exerted by child,
$F = 930\ \text{N} - 620\ \text{N} = 310$ N
Work done by child,
$W = Fd$
$= (310\ \text{N})(15\ \text{m}) = 4700\ \text{N}\cdot\text{m}$
$= 4700$ J

8. An adult exerts a force of 26 N to pull a child across the snow on a sled. The rope that joins the sled at an angle of 30.0° above horizontal. Ignoring friction, how much work is done in pulling the sled 390 m?

$W = (Fd)(\cos 30.0°)$
$= (0\ \text{N})(390\ \text{m})(0.866)$

$W = 0$ J

9. A grocer lifts an 8.0-kg carton from the floor to a height of 0.80 m, carries it 24 m across the store, and places it on a shelf 1.8 m above the floor. How much work does the grocer accomplish?

$W = Fd = (8.0\ \text{kg})(9.8\ \text{m/s}^2)(1.80\ \text{m}) = 140\ \text{N}\cdot\text{m} = 140$ J

Note: No work is done on the carton while it is carried horizontally.

10. At what speed can a 150-W motor lift a 2500-N load?

$$P = \frac{W}{t} = \frac{Fd}{t} = F\frac{d}{t} = Fv$$

$$v = \frac{P}{F} = \frac{150\ \text{W}}{2500\ \text{N}} = 0.060\ \frac{(\text{N}\cdot\text{m})/\text{s}}{\text{N}} = 0.060\ \text{m/s}$$

11. A mover pushes a 260-kg piano on wheels up a ramp 7.0 m long onto a stage 1.75 m above the auditorium floor. The mover pushes the piano with a force of 680 N.

a. How much work does the mover do?

$W_i = F_e d_e$
$= (680\ \text{N})(7.0\ \text{m})$
$= 4800\ \text{N}\cdot\text{m} = 4800$ J

b. What work is done on the piano by the machine?

$W_o = F_r d_r = m_r g d_r$
$= (260\ \text{kg})(9.8\ \text{m/s}^2)(1.75\ \text{m})$
$= 4500\ \text{N}\cdot\text{m} = 4500$ J

c. What is the efficiency of the machine?

efficiency $= \frac{W_o}{W_i} \times 100\%$
$= \frac{4500\ \text{J}}{4800\ \text{J}} \times 100\% = 94\%$

Date ______________ Period ______________ Name ______________

11 Chapter Assessment

Use with Chapter 11.

Energy

Understanding Concepts Part A

For each of the statements below, write true or rewrite the italicized part to make the statement true.

1. When you throw a ball into the air, its mechanical energy at any point is the *difference* in its kinetic energy and gravitational potential energy.

sum of

2. As an object falls towards Earth, the gravitational potential energy of the object *increases.*

decreases

3. The total amount of energy in an isolated, closed system *remains constant.*

true

4. If a tabletop is used as a reference point in a mechanical-energy problem, an object lying on the tabletop has a gravitational potential energy *greater than zero.*

equal to zero

5. Of the three sets of bar graphs below, an inelastic collision is represented by *set A.*

set B

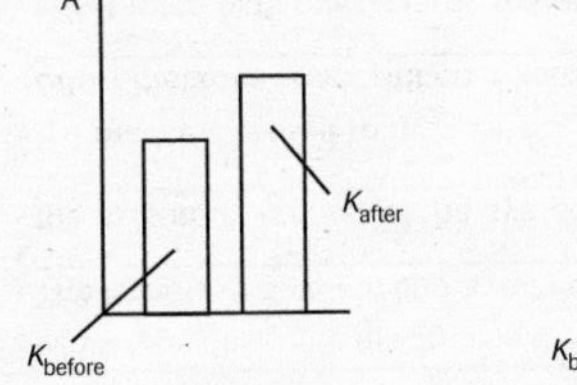

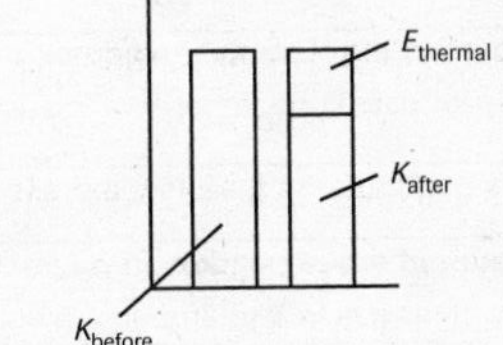

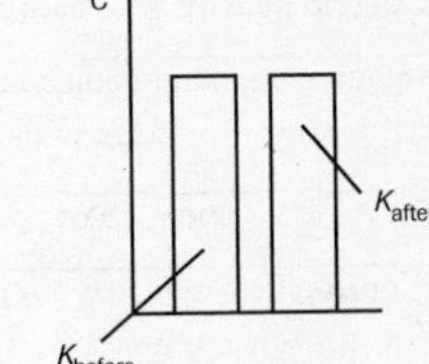

For each term on the left, write the letter of the matching item.

c 6. K

b 7. U_g

d 8. 1 joule

e 9. work-energy theorem

a 10. result of an elastic collision

a. $K_{after} = K_{before}$

b. $= mgh$

c. $= \frac{1}{2}mv^2$

d. $1\ \text{kg}\cdot\text{m}^2/\text{s}^2$

e. $Fd = \Delta K$

Name ________________

11 Chapter Assessment

Understanding Concepts Part B

Answer the following questions, showing your calculations.

1. Determine the mechanical energy of a 5.0-kg stone perched near the edge of a cliff 25.0 m high. Use the base of the cliff as the reference level.

   $K = \frac{1}{2}mv^2$ $\quad U_g = mgh$

   $= \frac{1}{2}(5.0 \text{ kg})(0.0 \text{ m/s})^2$ $\quad = (5.0 \text{ kg})(9.80 \text{ m/s}^2)(25.0 \text{ m})$

   $= 0.0 \text{ J}$ $\quad = 1.2 \times 10^3 \text{ J}$

   $E = K + U_g = 0.0 \text{ J} + (1.2 \times 10^3 \text{ J}) = 1.2 \times 10^3 \text{ J}$

2. Compare the kinetic energies of a biker and bike (with a combined mass of 80 kg) traveling at 3.00 m/s and the same biker and bike traveling twice as fast.

   $K_1 = \frac{1}{2}mv_1^2$ $\quad K_2 = \frac{1}{2}mv_2^2$

   $= \frac{1}{2}(80.0 \text{ kg})(3.00 \text{ m/s})^2$ $\quad = \frac{1}{2}(80.0 \text{ kg})(6.0 \text{ m/s})^2$

   $= 3.60 \times 10^2 \text{ J}$ $\quad = 1.44 \times 10^3 \text{ J}$

   $\frac{K_2}{K_1} = \frac{1.44 \times 10^3 \text{ J}}{3.60 \times 10^2 \text{ J}} = 4$

   $K_2 = 4K_1$

3. Which has the greater gravitational potential energy—a 550-g flower pot sitting on a 1.2-m high shelf or a 350-g flower pot sitting on a 1.8-m high shelf?

   $U_{g1} = m_1gh_1$ $\quad U_{g2} = m_2gh_2$

   $= (0.55 \text{ kg})(9.80 \text{ m/s}^2)(1.2 \text{ m})$ $\quad = (0.35 \text{ kg})(9.80 \text{ m/s}^2)(1.8 \text{ m})$

   $= 6.5 \text{ J}$ $\quad = 6.2 \text{ J}$

   The 550-g flower pot has greater gravitational potential energy.

4. A weight trainer lifts a 90.0-kg barbell from a stand 0.90 m high and raises it to a height of 1.75 m. What is the increase in the potential energy of the barbell?

   $\Delta U_g = U_{g2} - U_{g1} = mgh_2 - mgh_1 = mg\Delta h$

   $= (90.0 \text{ kg})(9.8 \text{ m/s}^2)(0.85 \text{ m})$

   $= 750 \text{ J}$

5. A child having a mass of 35.0 kg is on a sled having a mass of 5.0 kg. If the child and sled traveling together have a kinetic energy of 260 J, how fast are they moving?

   $K = \frac{1}{2}mv^2$ $\quad v = \sqrt{\frac{2K}{m}}$

   $= \sqrt{\frac{(2)(260 \text{ J})}{(40.0 \text{ kg})}} = \sqrt{\frac{(2)(260 \text{ kg}\cdot\text{m}^2/\text{s}^2)}{(40.0 \text{ kg})}}$

   $= 3.6 \text{ m/s}$

Name ________________

11 Chapter Assessment

Applying Concepts

Answer the following questions, using complete sentences.

1. Describe the energy changes that take place when the spring of a toy car is wound up and then released.

   The work done in winding the spring is changed to potential energy. When the spring is released, the potential energy stored in the wound spring is changed to the kinetic energy of the moving car.

2. Why must the first hill of a roller-coaster ride be the highest hill?

   The gravitational potential energy of the car at the top of the first hill is its mechanical energy for the entire ride. If any other hill were higher than the first one, the car would not have enough mechanical energy to reach the top of that hill.

3. Distinguish between an elastic collision and an inelastic collision.

   In an elastic collision, the kinetic energy of the colliding bodies after the collision is equal to their kinetic energy before the collision. In an inelastic collision, the kinetic energy of the bodies after the collision is less than the kinetic energy before the collision. In such a collision, some of the kinetic energy of the colliding bodies is transformed into thermal and acoustic energy.

4. A ball is thrown upward. Describe changes in its mechanical energy, kinetic energy, and gravitational potential energy between the time the ball is released and the time it reaches its maximum height.

   The mechanical energy of the ball is constant. The kinetic energy of the ball is maximum as it is released and decreases to zero as it reaches its maximum height. The gravitational energy can be considered zero at the point where the ball is released and increases to a maximum at its maximum height. Between any two points along its path, the decrease in its kinetic energy is equal to the increase in its gravitational potential energy, or vice versa.

Name ______________

11 Chapter Assessment

5. A block of wood rests on a frictionless surface and is attached to a spring, as shown below. When the spring is neither elongated nor compressed, the center of the block of wood is used as the reference point for the elastic potential energy of the block-and-spring system. The spring is then compressed to the left and released. Describe changes in the mechanical energy, kinetic energy, and elastic potential energy of the system between the time the spring is released and when it reaches its maximum elongation.

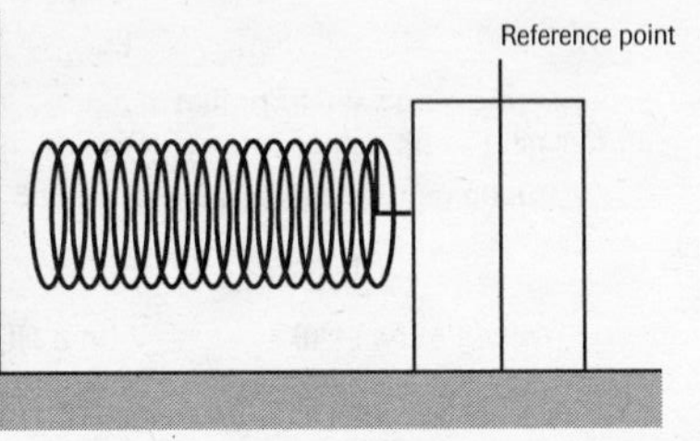

The mechanical energy of the block-and-spring system is constant. The kinetic energy of the system is zero as the spring is released, increases to a maximum as the block passes the reference point, and then decreases to zero as the spring reaches its maximum elongation. The elastic potential energy of the system is maximum when the spring is released, decreases to zero as the block passes through the reference point, and increases to a maximum as the spring reaches its maximum elongation. Between any two points along its path, the increase or decrease in the kinetic energy of the system is equal to an equal decrease or increase, respectively, in its elastic potential energy.

Name ______________

11 Chapter Assessment

Answer the following questions, showing your calculations.

6. Under what conditions will a 0.030-kg marble and a 3.00-kg rock have the same gravitational potential energy other than zero?

$K_1 = K_2$ $\quad m_1gh_1 = m_2gh_2$ $\quad h_1 = h_2\frac{m_2}{m_1}$

$h_1 = h_2\frac{(3.0\text{ kg})}{(0.030\text{ kg})} = 100\ h_2$

The two will have the same gravitational potential energy if the marble is raised to a point 100 times as high as the rock.

7. Under what conditions will a moving 0.030-kg marble and a moving 3.00-kg rock have the same kinetic energy?

$K_1 = K_2$ $\quad \frac{1}{2}m_1v_1^2 = \frac{1}{2}m_2v_2^2$

$v_1 = v_2\sqrt{\frac{3.0\text{ kg}}{0.030\text{ kg}}}$

$v_1 = 10v_2$

The two will have the same kinetic energy if the marble is traveling 10 times as fast as the rock.

8. During a contest that involved throwing a 7.0-kg bowling ball straight up in the air, one contestant exerted a force of 810 N on the ball. If the force was exerted through a distance of 2.0 m, how high did the ball go from the point of release?

$W = \Delta K$ $\qquad E_2 = E_3$

$Fd = K_2 - K_1 = K_2 - 0$ $\qquad K_2 + U_{g2} = K_3 + U_{g3}$

$Fd = K_2$ $\qquad$ or $K_2 + 0 = 0 + U_{g3}$

$K_2 = U_{g3}$

$\therefore Fd = mgh$

$h = \frac{Fd}{mg} = \frac{(810\text{ N})(2.0\text{ m})}{(7.0\text{ kg})(9.80\text{ m/s}^2)}$

$= 24\text{ m}$

11 Chapter Assessment

9. A 50.0-kg girl jumps onto a stationary 2.4-kg skateboard at 4.1 m/s. Determine the fraction of the original kinetic energy that was lost due to the inelastic nature of the collision.

$p_{after} = p_{before}$

$(m_1 + m_2)v_{after} = m_1v_1 + 0$

$v_{after} = \frac{m_1v_1}{(m_1 + m_2)}$

$= \frac{(50.0\ kg)(4.1\ m/s)}{(50.0\ kg + 2.4\ kg)}$

$= 3.9\ m/s$

$K_{before} = \frac{1}{2}m_1v_1^2$

$= \frac{1}{2}(50.0\ kg)(4.1\ m/s)^2$

$= 420\ J$

$K_{after} = \frac{1}{2}(m_1 + m_2)v_{after}^2$

$= 400\ J$

$\Delta K = K_{after} - K_{before} = 400\ J - 420\ J$

$= -20\ J$

$\frac{\Delta K}{K_{before}} = \frac{-20\ J}{420\ J} = -0.05$

5% was lost.

10. A 50.0-kg skater and skateboard leaves the right side of the ramp shown below at a speed of 7.0 m/s. If the ramp is frictionless, what was his initial speed down the opposite side of the ramp?

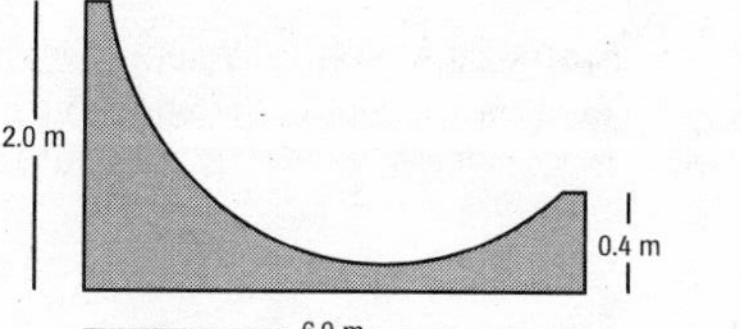

$E_{after} = E_{before}$

$K_{after} + U_{g\ after} = K_{before} + U_{g\ before}$

$K_{before} = K_{after} + U_{g\ after} - U_{g\ before}$

$\therefore K_{before} = \frac{1}{2}mv_2^2 + mgh_2 - mgh_1$

$K_{before} = \frac{1}{2}mv_2^2 + mg(h_2 - h_1)$

$= \frac{1}{2}(50.0\ kg)(6.2\ m/s)^2 + (50.0\ kg)(9.80\ m/s^2)(0.4\ m - 2.0 m)$

$= 960\ J - 780\ J = 180\ J$

$K_{before} = \frac{1}{2}mv_1^2 \qquad v_1 = \sqrt{\frac{2K_{before}}{m}} = \sqrt{\frac{(2)(180\ J)}{(50.0\ kg)}}$

$= 2.7\ m/s$

12 Chapter Assessment

Use with Chapter 12.

Thermal Energy

Understanding Concepts Part A

Write the letter of the choice that best completes each statement.

d 1. The measure of the hotness of an object is its ____.
- a. entropy
- b. heat of vaporization
- c. specific heat
- d. temperature

a 2. The amount of heat needed to melt 1 kg of a substance is the ____.
- a. heat of fusion
- b. entropy
- c. heat of vaporization
- d. specific heat

b 3. A heat engine continuously converts ____.
- a. mechanical energy to thermal energy
- b. thermal energy to mechanical energy
- c. entropy to thermal energy
- d. heat to temperature

a 4. Entropy is the measure of a system's ____.
- a. disorder
- b. temperature
- c. thermal energy
- d. thermal equilibrium

c 5. Energy that flows as a result of a difference in temperature is called ____.
- a. entropy
- b. heat
- c. kinetic energy
- d. specific heat

c 6. Two objects are in thermal equilibrium if they ____.
- a. contain the same number of particles
- b. have the same thermal energy
- c. are at the same temperature
- d. have the same entropy

For each of the statements below, write true *or* false.

7. **true** According to the second law of thermodynamics, natural processes go in a direction that maintains or increases the total entropy of the universe.

8. **false** The total increase in the thermal energy of a system is the work done on it minus the heat added to it.

9. **true** A heat pump is a refrigerator that can be run in two directions.

10. **true** An increase in the average kinetic energy of particles means an increase in temperature.

11. **false** Convection typically takes place in solids.

12. **false** A thermometer is used to measure heat.

Name ______________________

12 Chapter Assessment

Understanding Concepts Part B

Answer the following questions, showing your calculations.

1. Helium has the lowest boiling point of all elements. It boils at −269°C. Express that temperature in kelvins.

   $T_K = T_C + 273$

   $T_K = -269°C + 273$

   $= 4\ K$

2. The specific heat of methanol is 2450 J/kg·K. Calculate the amount of heat that must be added to 0.25 kg of methanol to raise its temperature by 15°C.

   $Q = mC\Delta T = (0.25\ kg)(2450\ J/kg{\cdot}K)(15\ °C)\ 1K/°C = 9.2 \times 10^3\ J$

3. Ice has a specific heat of 2060 J/kg·K. How much heat must be absorbed by 2.0 kg of ice at −20.0°C to raise it up to 0.0°C, before any melting actually takes place?

   $Q = mC\Delta T = (2.0\ kg)(2060\ J/kg{\cdot}K)(20.0\ °C)\ 1K/°C = 8.2 \times 10^4\ J$

4. Given that ice has a heat of fusion of 3.34×10^5 J/kg, how much more heat must be added to the ice in problem 3 to change it to liquid water at 0.0°C?

   $Q = mH_f = (2.0\ kg)(3.34 \times 10^5\ J/kg) = 6.7 \times 10^5\ J$

5. The heat of vaporization of water is 2.26×10^6 J/kg. How much heat must be added to 1.5 kg of liquid water at 100°C to change it to steam at the same temperature?

   $Q = mH_v = (1.5\ kg)(2.26 \times 10^6\ J/kg) = 3.4 \times 10^6\ J$

6. Iron has a heat of fusion of 2.66×10^5 J/kg. How much heat must be removed from 7.94 kg of molten iron at its freezing point to turn it into solid iron at the same temperature?

   $Q = -mH_f = -(7.94\ kg)(2.66 \times 10^5\ J/kg) = -2.11 \times 10^6\ J$

Name ______________________

12 Chapter Assessment

Applying Concepts

Answer the following questions, using complete sentences.

1. Distinguish between thermal energy, temperature, and heat.

   The thermal energy of an object is the overall energy of motion of the particles that make it up. The temperature is a measure of the average kinetic energy of the particles. Heat is the energy that flows between objects as a result of a difference in temperature.

2. Explain what is meant by the kinetic-molecular theory and how it applies to the study of thermal energy.

   According to the kinetic-molecular theory, matter is made up of tiny particles that are in constant motion. These particles have kinetic energy due to their motion and vibration. The particles also have potential energy. The sum of the kinetic and potential energies of the particles that make up a sample of matter is the thermal energy of that sample.

3. Explain what is meant by absolute zero. What is its value on the Celsius scale and on the Kelvin scale?

   Absolute zero is the temperature at which all thermal energy has been removed from a substance. Absolute zero is −273.15°C, or 0 K.

4. Equal masses of methanol and liquid water initially at the same temperature are heated by the same heat source. The specific heat of methanol is 2450 J/kg·K, and that of water is 4180 J/kg·K. Compare the temperatures of these two substances after they are heated for the same period of time. Give a reason for your answer.

   The temperature of the alcohol will be higher than that of the water. Alcohol has a lower specific heat than water, so the temperature of a given mass of alcohol will increase more than that of an equal mass of water when the same amount of heat is added to each substance.

5. A sample of iron at a temperature of 225 K is placed in a container of water at a temperature of 350 K. Describe what will take place in terms of heat transfer and temperature.

   Heat will be transferred from the warmer material to the cooler material—from the water to the iron. At equilibrium, the temperature of the two substances will be equal and will have some value between 225 K and 350 K.

6. How does the entropy of a system change when heat is removed from the system?

   When heat is removed from a system, the average kinetic energy of the particles is decreased, the particles slow down, and the system becomes more orderly. Thus, the entropy of the system decreases.

Name ____________

12 Chapter Assessment

Answer the following questions, showing your calculations.

7. A 4.0-kg iron ball at 225°C is placed in a container of liquid water at 4°C. When the system reaches thermal equilibrium, its temperature is 45°C. What is the mass of water in the container? The specific heat of iron is 450 J/kg·K, and the specific heat of water is 4180 J/kg·K.

$m_w C_w \Delta T_w = -m_i C_i \Delta T_i$

$m_w = \frac{-m_i C_i \Delta T_i}{C_w \Delta T_w}$

$= \frac{-(4.0\ \text{kg})(450\ \text{J/kg·K})(225°\text{C} - 45°\text{C})}{(4180\ \text{J/kg·K})(4°\text{C} - 45°\text{C})} = 1.9\ \text{kg}$

8. A 2.0-kg cube of iron at 300.0°C is placed on a 5-kg block of ice at 0.0°C. How much ice will change to liquid water at 0.0°C? The specific heat of iron is 450 J/kg·K, and the heat of fusion of ice is 3.34×10^5 J/kg.

The heat given off by the iron, which goes from 300.0°C to 0.0°C, is

$Q = mC\Delta T = (2.0\ \text{kg})(450\ \text{J/kg · K})(-300.0\ °\text{C})\ (1\text{K}/1°\text{C})$

$= -2.7 \times 10^5\ \text{J}$

This heat is taken up by the ice, which thus absorbs 2.7×10^5 J.

$Q = mH_f \qquad m = \frac{Q}{H_f} \qquad = \frac{2.7 \times 10^5\ \text{J}}{3.34 \times 10^5\ \text{J/kg}}$

$= 0.81\ \text{kg}$

9. How much heat is absorbed in changing 2.00 kg of ice at –5.0°C to steam at 110.0°C? The specific heats of ice, liquid water, and steam are, respectively, 2060 J/kg·K, 4180 J/kg·K, and 2020 J/kg·K. The heat of fusion of ice is 3.34×10^5 J/kg. The heat of vaporization of water is 2.26×10^6 J/kg.

$Q = mC\Delta T_{ice} + mH_f + mC\Delta T_{water} + mH_v + mC\Delta T_{steam}$

$= [(2.00\ \text{kg})(2060\ \text{J/kg · K})(5.0\ °\text{C})(1\text{K}/1°\text{C})] + [(2.00\ \text{kg})(3.34 \times 10^5\ \text{J/kg})]$

$+ [2.00\ \text{kg})(4180\ \text{J/kg · K})(100.0\ °\text{C})(1\text{K}/1°\text{C})] + [(2.00\ \text{kg})(2.26 \times 10^6\ \text{J/kg})]$

$+ [(2.00\ \text{kg})(2020\ \text{J/kg · K})(10.0\ °\text{C})(1\text{K}/1°\text{C})]$

$= 6.1 \times 10^6\ \text{J}$

10. How much heat must be added to 1.5 kg of liquid water at 95.0°C to change it to steam at 100.0°C? The specific heat of liquid water is 4180 J/kg·K. The heat of vaporization of water is 2.26×10^6 J/kg.

$Q = mC\Delta T + mH_v$

$= [(1.5\ \text{kg})(4180\ \text{J/kg · K})(5.0\ °\text{C})(1\text{K}/1°\text{C})] + [(1.5\ \text{kg})(2.26 \times 10^6\ \text{J/kg})]$

$= 3.4 \times 10^6\ \text{J}$

Date ____________ Period ____________ Name ____________

13 Chapter Assessment

Use with Chapter 13.

States of Matter

Understanding Concepts Part A

Write the letter of the choice that best completes the statement or answers the question.

c **1.** At sea level, if the area of a surface increases, the pressure of the atmosphere on the surface ____.
a. increases **b.** decreases **c.** stays the same

d **2.** Pressure is equal to ____.
a. force plus area **c.** force minus area
b. force times area **d.** force divided by area

a **3.** The SI unit of pressure is the ____.
a. pascal **b.** atmosphere **c.** millibar **d.** newton

d **4.** According to Pascal's principle, any change on a confined fluid ____.
a. is directly proportional to the volume of the fluid
b. is inversely proportional to the volume of the fluid
c. depends on the shape of the container
d. is transmitted unchanged throughout the fluid

b **5.** The buoyant force exerted on an object immersed in a fluid is equal to the ____.
a. volume of the displaced fluid **c.** weight of the immersed object
b. weight of the displaced fluid **d.** mass of the immersed object

b **6.** According to Bernoulli's principle, as the velocity of a fluid increases, the ____.
a. density of the fluid decreases
b. pressure exerted by the fluid decreases
c. mass of the fluid increases
d. buoyant force of the fluid decreases

For each of the statements below, write true *or rewrite the italicized part to make the statement true.*

7. **true** As heat is applied to a sample of liquid water at 1°C, the volume of the water *decreases*.

8. **solids** A crystal lattice is a characteristic of many *gases*.

9. **true** An object that is deformed by a force and returns to its original form when the force is removed is exhibiting the property of *elasticity*.

10. **plasma** The *liquid* state is the state of matter in which electrons have been torn away from the atoms.

11. **cohesive** The *adhesive* forces within a liquid account for surface tension.

Name ______________

13 Chapter Assessment

Understanding Concepts Part B

Answer the following questions, showing your calculations.

1. Atmospheric pressure at sea level is about 1.0×10^5 Pa. How much force does the atmosphere exert on a driveway that is 18.0 m long and 5.0 m wide?

$$P = \frac{F}{A}$$
$$F = PA$$
$$= (1.0 \times 10^5\ \text{Pa})(18.0\ \text{m})(5.0\ \text{m})$$
$$= 9.0 \times 10^6\ \text{N}$$

2. Find the total force exerted by Earth's atmosphere on the top and sides of a rectangular can. The base of the can is 10.0 cm wide and 15.0 cm long, and the can is 12.0 cm high.

total area of top and sides $= 2lh + 2wh + wl$
$$= (2)(15.0\ \text{cm})(12.0\ \text{cm}) + (2)(10.0\ \text{cm})(12.0\ \text{cm}) + (10.0\ \text{cm})(15.0\ \text{cm})$$
$$= 7.50 \times 10^2\ \text{cm}^2$$
$$F = PA$$
$$= (1.0 \times 10^5\ \text{Pa})(7.50 \times 10^2\ \text{cm}^2)$$
$$7.5 \times 10^7\ \text{N}$$

3. A force of 400.0 N is exerted on a small piston that has an area of 8.0 cm². How much weight can be lifted on a large piston to which the force is transmitted, given that the large piston has an area of 20.0 cm²?

$$\frac{F_1}{A_1} = \frac{F_2}{A_2} \qquad F_2 = \frac{F_1 A_2}{A_1}$$
$$= \frac{(400.0\ \text{N})(20.0\ \text{cm}^2)}{8.0\ \text{cm}^2} = 1.0 \times 10^3\ \text{N}$$

4. The area of a small piston is 4.0 cm². A force of 150 N on the small piston will move a weight of 1200 N on a large piston. What is the area of the large piston?

$$A_2 = \frac{F_2 A_1}{F_1}$$
$$= \frac{(1200\ \text{N})(4.0\ \text{cm}^2)}{150\ \text{N}}$$
$$= 32\ \text{cm}^2$$

Name ______________

13 Chapter Assessment

5. A cube of lead that is 10.0 cm on each edge is suspended from a line and immersed in water. How much force is exerted on the line holding the lead cube? The density of lead is 11.3×10^3 kg/m³.

$$V_{water} = l_{lead}^3$$
$$= (0.100\ \text{m})^3 = 1.00 \times 10^{-3}\ \text{m}^3$$
$$F_{buoyant} = \rho_{water} V_{water} g$$
$$= (1.00 \times 10^3\ \text{kg/m}^3)(1.00 \times 10^{-3}\ \text{m}^3)(9.80\ \text{m/s}^2)$$
$$= 9.80\ \text{N}$$
$$F_g = \rho_{lead} V_{lead} g$$
$$= (11.3 \times 10^3\ \text{kg/m}^3)(1.00 \times 10^{-3}\ \text{m}^3)(9.80\ \text{m/s}^2)$$
$$= 111\ \text{N}$$
$$F_{apparent} = F_g - F_{buoyant}$$
$$= 111\ \text{N} - 9.80\ \text{N}$$
$$= 101\ \text{N}$$

6. An iron bar 1.6 m long at room temperature (20°C) is heated uniformly along its entire length until its temperature reaches 1250°C. How much longer is the bar at the higher temperature? The coefficient of linear expansion of iron is 1.2×10^{-5} (°C)$^{-1}$.

$$\Delta L = \alpha L_i \Delta T$$
$$= (1.2 \times 10^{-5}\ (°\text{C})^{-1})(1.6\ \text{m})(1230°\text{C})$$
$$= 2.4 \times 10^{-2}\ \text{m}$$

Name ______________

13 Chapter Assessment

Applying Concepts

Answer the following questions, using complete sentences.

1. What does the kinetic-molecular theory of matter say about gases?

The particles that make up a gas are in constant, random, high-speed motion and are widely separated. All collisions among particles or between gas particles and the walls of the container that holds them are elastic and result in no loss of kinetic energy.

2. Most automobile brake systems are hydraulic systems. Explain how the relatively small force involved in pressing on a brake pedal can give the brakes enough force to stop the car.

The brake system of an automobile is a fluid-filled system. Pressure exerted on the brake pedal is transferred to a small piston inside the master cylinder and then throughout the enclosed fluid of the brake system, which contains larger pistons that exert force against the mechanical portions of the brakes. The larger area of these pistons results in an increase of total force sufficient to create enough friction to slow and eventually stop a car.

3. An iron cube weighing 5 N is suspended from a string and lowered into a container of water until the cube is completely immersed. Describe what seems to happen to the weight of the cube. Give a reason for your answer.

The weight of the cube seems to decrease. The cube is buoyed up by a force equal to the weight of the water it displaces. This buoyant force acts in the direction opposite to that of gravity, thereby decreasing the apparent weight of the object.

Name ______________

13 Chapter Assessment

4. What properties can be used to distinguish between gases and liquids? What properties do gases and liquids have in common that allow them to be classified as fluids?

A liquid has a definite volume; a gas takes the volume of the container that holds it. The particles of a liquid are much closer together than those of a gas, so a liquid is much less compressible than a gas. The properties that make liquids and gases fluids are the ability to flow and to change shape.

5. How is matter in the plasma state similar to matter in the gas state? How is it different?

Both are fluid states. The particles of matter in both states are far apart and in rapid, random motion. However, the particles in a plasma are electrons and positively charged ions rather than neutral particles.

6. Explain the principle behind the operation of a bimetallic strip.

Different materials have different coefficients of thermal expansion. A temperature change makes the different metals in a bimetallic strip expand by different amounts, causing bending that can be used to break or complete an electric circuit.

Name ______________________

13 Chapter Assessment

Answer the following questions, showing your calculations.

7. A cylindrical water tank 20.0 m high has a diameter of 14.0 m. The tank is full of water. What is the pressure at the bottom of the tank?

$P = \rho hg$

$= (1.00 \times 10^3\ \text{kg/m}^3)(20.0\ \text{m})(9.80\ \text{m/s}^2) = 1.96 \times 10^5\ \text{Pa}$

8. A rectangular solid measures 1.20 m by 0.80 m by 0.20 m. When the solid is standing on its smallest face, it exerts a pressure of 5.2×10^3 Pa. How much does the solid weigh?

$P = \frac{F}{A}$

$F = PA$

$= (5.2 \times 10^3\ \text{N/m}^2)(0.80\ \text{m})(0.20\ \text{m})$

$= 8.3 \times 10^2\ \text{N}$

9. What is the density of the solid in problem 8?

$\rho = \frac{m}{V}$ $\quad m = \frac{F}{g}$

$\rho = \frac{F}{gV}$

$\frac{8.3 \times 10^2\ \text{kg}\cdot\text{m/s}^2}{(9.8\ \text{m/s}^2)(1.20\ \text{m})(0.80\ \text{m})(0.20\ \text{m})}$

$= 4.4 \times 10^2\ \text{kg/m}^3$

10. A volume of 200.0 cm^3 of water at a temperature of 4°C is in a container with a 1000-cm^3 capacity. The container and its contents are heated to 95°C. What is the final volume of water in the container? The coefficient of volume expansion of water is $210 \times 10^{-6}(°\text{C})^{-1}$.

$\Delta V = \beta V \Delta T$

$= (210 \times 10^{-6}\ (°\text{C})^{-1})(200.0\ \text{cm}^3)(91°\text{C})$

$= 3.8\ \text{cm}^3$

$V_f = 200.0\ \text{cm}^3 + 3.8\ \text{cm}^3$

$= 203.8\ \text{cm}^3$

Date ____________ Period ____________ Name ______________________

14 Chapter Assessment

Use with Chapter 14.

Waves and Energy Transfer

Understanding Concepts Part A

Write the letter of the choice that best completes the statement or answers the question.

c **1.** Which of the following usually transmits energy without transferring matter?
a. particle **b.** electron **c.** wave **d.** proton

c **2.** The time interval during which wave motion repeats is the _____.
a. wave pulse **b.** frequency **c.** period **d.** wavelength

b **3.** The number of vibrations per second is the _____.
a. amplitude **b.** frequency **c.** period **d.** wavelength

a **4.** The speed of any mechanical wave depends on _____.
a. the medium through which it travels **c.** its angle of reflection
b. its amplitude **d.** its energy

a **5.** When light from the air enters a body of water, in what form does some of the energy move back into the air?
a. reflected wave **c.** incident wave
b. transmitted wave **d.** sound wave

c **6.** Which of the following may be produced during destructive interference of waves?
a. a reflection **c.** a node
b. a higher crest **d.** a lower trough

b **7.** The change in wave direction at the boundary of two different media is _____.
a. incidence **b.** refraction **c.** reflection **d.** diffraction

d **8.** The spreading of waves around the edge of a barrier is _____.
a. incidence **b.** refraction **c.** reflection **d.** diffraction

For each of the statements below, write true *or rewrite the italicized part to make the statement true.*

9. **increases** Increasing the amplitude of a wave *decreases* the rate of energy transfer.

10. **true** Frequency is *inversely* related to period.

11. **meters** Wavelength is measured in *hertz*.

12. **true** Wave speed equals *frequency* times wavelength.

13. **normal** The *node* is a line at a right angle to the barrier.

Name ______________

14 Chapter Assessment

Understanding Concepts Part B

Answer the following questions, showing your calculations.

1. A note on a piano vibrates 262 times per second. What is the period of the wave?

   $T = 1/f$
   $= 1/(262\ Hz)$
   $= 3.82 \times 10^{-3}\ s$

2. If sound travels at 5600 m/s through a steel rod, what is the wavelength, given a wave frequency of 2480 Hz?

   $v = \lambda f$
   $\lambda = \frac{v}{f}$
   $= \frac{5600\ m/s}{2480\ Hz}$
   $= 2.3\ m$

3. What is the speed of a wave that has a frequency of 3.7×10^3 Hz and a wavelength of 1.2×10^{-2} m?

   $v = \lambda f$
   $= (1.2 \times 10^{-2}\ m)(3.7 \times 10^3\ Hz)$
   $= 44\ m/s$

4. A beam of light strikes a mirror, making an angle of 43° relative to the normal. What is the angle between the normal and the reflected ray?

   angle of reflection = angle of incidence
   = 43°

5. The wavelength of a water wave is 4.0×10^2 m. The wave is approaching land at 25 m/s. What is the period?

   $T = 1/f$ $\quad f = v/\lambda$
   $T = \lambda/v$
   $= \frac{4.0 \times 10^2\ m}{25.0\ m/s}$
   $= 16\ s$

6. The wavelength of a sound produced by a tuning fork is 1.30 m. The fork has a frequency of 256 Hz. What is the wave velocity?

   $v = \lambda f$
   $= (1.30\ m)(256\ Hz)$
   $= 333\ m/s$

Name ______________

14 Chapter Assessment

Applying Concepts

Answer the following questions, using complete sentences.

1. Describe the relationship between the amplitude of a wave and the energy that is transferred by the wave.

   The greater the amplitude is, the greater is the amount of energy transferred.

2. Suppose two boats are a few meters apart and lie along a line perpendicular to the shore. Describe their motion if they are subjected to passing ocean waves whose wavelength is not equal to the distance between the boats. Will the oscillations of the two boats have the same amplitudes and frequencies?

   The boats will bob up and down as the waves pass. The repeated bobbing, or oscillations, will have the same amplitude and frequency, although the two boats will not generally crest or trough at the same time.

3. Contrast the reflection of a wave that passes from one medium into a lighter, more flexible medium to a wave that passes from one medium into a heavier and stiffer medium.

   The reflected wave would not be inverted if the wave passed into a lighter, more flexible medium. The reflected wave would be inverted if the second medium were heavier and stiffer than the original medium.

4. What is the principle of superposition, and how is it related to interference?

   The principle of superposition states that a medium's displacement caused by two or more waves is the algebraic sum of the displacement caused by each wave. Interference, both constructive and destructive, is the result of the superposition of waves.

5. Describe a standing wave and explain how it can be produced.

   A standing wave appears to be staying still. It has nodes at the ends and one or more antinodes in between. One type of standing wave can be produced by adjusting the rate of motion of the oscillator (for example, a hand shaking a rope) so that the period equals the time needed for the wave to make one round-trip from the oscillator to the other end and back again.

6. Describe what occurs if waves pass through two closely spaced holes in a barrier.

   Diffraction occurs at each hole, producing two sets of circular waves that interfere constructively and destructively with each other. Alternating lines of nodes and of antinodes radiate from the barrier.

Name ______________________

14 Chapter Assessment

Answer the following questions, showing your calculations.

7. Suppose you set a cup of milk on the kitchen counter while the dishwasher is running. You notice that the vibration of the dishwasher causes standing waves in the milk. The crests of the waves form four concentric rings. The radius of the cup is 3.0 cm, and the speed of the wave in the liquid is 1.5 m/s. What is the frequency of the vibrations coming from the dishwasher? (Hint: Think in terms of how many wavelengths lie along the radius.)

$\lambda = (3.0\text{ cm})/4 = 0.75\text{ cm} = 7.5 \times 10^{-3}\text{ m}$

$f = v/\lambda$

$= \dfrac{1.5\text{ m/s}}{7.5 \times 10^{-3}\text{ m}}$

$= 2.0 \times 10^{2}\text{ Hz}$

8. The average distance between Earth and the moon is 384 790 km. If Earth's atmosphere were uniform and extended to the moon's surface, how many seconds would it take sound to travel from Earth to the moon? How many days would that equal? Assume that the speed of sound is 343 m/s.

$\Delta t = \dfrac{\Delta d}{v}$

$= \dfrac{3.8479 \times 10^{5}\text{ km}}{(343\text{ m/s})(1.00 \times 10^{-3}\text{ km/m})}$

$= 1.12 \times 10^{6}\text{ s}$

$\dfrac{1.12 \times 10^{6}\text{ s}}{8.64 \times 10^{4}\text{ s/day}} = 13.0\text{ days}$

9. Waves traveling along a long string are reflected from the fixed end. They produce a standing wave that has a wavelength of 2.4 m. How far from the fixed end are the first two antinodes? Note that there is a node at the fixed end.

If the fixed end of the string is a node, the first antinode must be one-quarter of a wavelength away, or (2.4 m)/4 = 0.60 m from the end. The second antinode must be one-half of a wavelength farther along, or (2.4 m)/2 = 1.2 m from the first antinode, or 0.60 m + 1.2 m = 1.8 m from the end.

10. Two dissimilar springs are tied together. A wave is started on the first spring. The wavelength is 0.20 m, and the speed is 5.0 m/s. When the wave reaches the second spring, it moves along that spring at a speed of 7.5 m/s. What is the wavelength of the wave in the second spring?

Let the subscript 1 stand for the first spring, and 2 stand for the second spring.

$f_1 = \dfrac{v_1}{\lambda_1}$

$= \dfrac{5.0\text{ m/s}}{0.20\text{m}} = 25\text{ Hz}$, so f_2 also equals 25 Hz.

$\lambda_2 = \dfrac{v_2}{f_2}$

$= \dfrac{7.5\text{ m/s}}{25\text{ Hz}} = 0.30\text{ m}$

Date ____________ Period ____________ Name ______________________

15 Chapter Assessment

Use with Chapter 15.

Sound

Understanding Concepts Part A

Write the letter of the choice that best completes the statement or answers the question.

d 1. Echoes demonstrate which behavior of sound waves?
a. refraction b. diffraction c. interference d. reflection

c 2. Sound is an example of what kind of wave?
a. transverse b. electromagnetic c. longitudinal d. surface

c 3. As an approaching ambulance passes an unmoving observer, what happens to the apparent pitch of the sound emitted by the ambulance siren, as heard by the observer?
a. It increases. c. It decreases.
b. It stays the same. d. It becomes inaudible.

b 4. A detected apparent change in the pitch caused by the motion of a sound source or of an observer is called _____.
a. refraction c. reflection
b. the Doppler shift d. diffraction

a 5. The pitch of a sound depends most directly upon the sound's _____.
a. frequency b. speed c. amplitude d. loudness

c 6. If two notes have a frequency ratio of 1:2, the notes differ by a(n) _____.
a. major third b. fifth c. octave d. fourth

b 7. If two notes have a frequency ratio of 2:3, the notes differ by a(n) _____.
a. major third b. fifth c. octave d. fourth

c 8. Approximately how many times greater is the pressure amplitude of a 40-dB sound than that of a 20-dB sound?
a. 5 b. 20 c. 10 d. 100

For each of the statements below, write true *or* false.

9. **false** The outermost structure of the human ear that is used to collect sound waves is called the cochlea.

10. **true** Tone quality or tone color is also called timbre.

11. **true** For an open-pipe resonator, a column of length $\frac{1}{2}$ will resonate with a tuning fork.

12. **false** The frequency of a beat is the sum of the frequencies of the two waves that produce it.

Name ____________________

15 Chapter Assessment

Understanding Concepts Part B

Answer the following questions, showing your calculations.

1. A sound wave traveling at a speed of 340.0 m/s has a wavelength of 1.25 m. What is the frequency of the sound?

$$f = \frac{v}{\lambda} = \frac{340.0\ \text{m/s}}{1.25\ \text{m}} = 272\ \text{Hz}$$

2. How long is a wave that has the same frequency as the one in problem 1 and that is traveling through water at 1435 m/s?

$$\lambda = \frac{v}{f} = \frac{1435\ \text{m/s}}{272\ \text{Hz}} = 5.28\ \text{m}$$

3. A note on the piano has a frequency of 55 Hz. What is the frequency of the note that is three octaves higher?

$55\ \text{Hz} \times 2 \times 2 \times 2 = 440\ \text{Hz}$

4. What is the wavelength of a sound made by a violin string vibrating at 640 Hz if the wave is traveling at 350 m/s?

$$\lambda = \frac{v}{f} = \frac{350\ \text{m/s}}{640\ \text{Hz}} = 0.55\ \text{m}$$

5. What is the period of the sound wave in problem 4?

$$T = \frac{1}{f} = \frac{1}{640\ \text{Hz}} = 1.6 \times 10^{-3}\ \text{s}$$

6. A 448-Hz tuning fork and a 444-Hz tuning fork are struck at the same time. What is the frequency of the beat produced?

$$f_{beat} = |f_A - f_B| = |448\ \text{Hz} - 444\ \text{Hz}| = 4\ \text{Hz}$$

7. Two tuning forks struck simultaneously produce a beat with a frequency of 2 Hz. The frequency of one fork is 364 Hz. What are the two possible frequencies of the other tuning fork?

$$f_{beat} = |f_A - f_B|$$

$$\text{so } f_B = f_A \pm |f_A - f_B| = 364\ \text{Hz} \pm 2\ \text{Hz} = 366\ \text{Hz or } 362\ \text{Hz}$$

Name ____________________

15 Chapter Assessment

Applying Concepts

Answer the following questions, using complete sentences.

1. In terms of resonance, pitch, and frequency, describe how sound is produced in a trumpet.

When the trumpet is played, air within the tube vibrates in resonance with the vibrating lips of the player. The player varies the pitch by changing the length of the air column, which in turn determines the resonant frequencies of the vibrating air.

2. How do molecules in air allow a distant listener to hear a trumpet?

When the trumpet is blown, the vibrating instrument produces regular variations in air pressure that extend beyond the instrument. As the molecules in the outside air collide, they transmit pressure oscillations away from the trumpet, to the ear of the listener.

3. Explain how and why the apparent pitch of a whistle of a moving train is different for a person standing on the platform ahead of the train, for a person standing behind the train, and for a person on the train.

The person standing ahead of the train will hear a pitch that is above the actual pitch of the whistle because of the Doppler shift: the source's motion toward the listener compresses the wavelength, raising the apparent frequency, which determines the pitch heard. The person standing behind the train will hear a pitch that is below the actual pitch because the effect of the source's motion away from the listener is to lengthen the wavelength, lowering the apparent frequency. The person in the train is moving at the same speed as the sound source and will hear a pitch that corresponds to the actual frequency of the source.

4. Contrast the harmonics of open-pipe resonators with the harmonics of closed-pipe resonators.

Open-pipe resonators with a fundamental frequency f have the harmonics $2f_1$, $3f_1$, $4f_1$, and so on. Closed-pipe resonators have frequencies that are odd-number multiples of the fundamental: $3f_1$, $5f_1$, and so on.

5. Describe the decibel scale and its relationship to actual pressure amplitude and perceived loudness.

The decibel scale is a logarithmic scale that measures sound level in terms of pressure amplitudes. The faintest sound audible to people is assigned a value of 0 dB. Multiplying actual pressure amplitude by 10 corresponds to an increase of 20 dB. However, most people perceive each 10-dB increase as a doubling of loudness.

Name ______

15 Chapter Assessment

Answer the following questions, showing your calculations.

6. The speed of sound through air depends on air temperature. At 20°C, sound waves travel through air at 343 m/s. What is the temperature of the air if the speed of sound is 351 m/s? Assume that the velocity of sound in air increases 0.60 m/s for each increase of 1°C.

$$T = \frac{351\ \text{m/s} - 343\ \text{m/s}}{0.60\ \text{m/s}\cdot{}^\circ\text{C}} + 20^\circ\text{C}$$
$$= 33^\circ\text{C}$$

7. A tuning fork has a frequency of 365 Hz. In an air column, the fork causes the loudest sounds at resonant lengths that are separated by 45.6 cm. What is the velocity of the sound? Recall that resonance lengths are spaced by half-wavelength intervals.

$$l_B - l_A = \lambda/2$$
$$\lambda = 2(0.456\ \text{m}) = 0.912\ \text{m}$$
$$v = \lambda f$$
$$= (0.912\ \text{m})(365\ \text{Hz})$$
$$= 333\ \text{m/s}$$

8 A tuning fork with a frequency of 365 Hz is held above an air column. What is the spacing between resonant lengths if the air temperature is 15°C? Assume that the speed of sound in air changes by 0.60 m/s for each 1°C change of temperature.

$$v = 343\ \text{m/s} + (0.60\ \text{m/s}\cdot{}^\circ\text{C})(-5^\circ\text{C})$$
$$= 340\ \text{m/s}$$
$$\lambda = \frac{v}{f}$$
$$= \frac{340\ \text{m/s}}{365\ \text{Hz}}$$
$$= 0.932\ \text{m}$$
$$l_B - l_A = \lambda/2$$
$$= \frac{0.932\ \text{m}}{2}$$
$$= 0.466\ \text{m}$$

9. A note has a frequency of 326 Hz. What is the frequency of a note that is one octave lower? What is the frequency of a note that is a fifth higher than the note?

octave ratio of frequencies = 1:2

f for note an octave lower = (1/2)(326 Hz) = 163 Hz

fifth ratio of frequencies = 2:3

f for note a fifth higher = (3/2)(326 Hz) = 489 Hz

Date ______ Period ______ Name ______

16 Chapter Assessment

Use with Chapter 16.

Light

Understanding Concepts Part A

Write the letter of the choice that best completes the statement or answers the question.

a 1. What kind of wave is light?
a. electromagnetic b. mechanical c. surface d. longitudinal

d 2. The wavelength of red light is approximately ____.
a. 200 nm b. 400 nm c. 500 nm d. 700 nm

b 3. Which of the following characteristics of light has a defined value?
a. wavelength c. frequency
b. speed in a vacuum d. amplitude

a 4. The rate, in lumens, at which light is emitted from a lightbulb is the bulb's ____.
a. luminous flux c. frequency
b. illuminance d. luminous intensity

d 5. Illumination under a small light source is proportional to ____.
a. r b. r^2 c. $1/r$ d. $1/r^2$

b 6. Very thin white tissue paper can best be described as ____.
a. transparent b. translucent c. opaque d. luminous

c 7 Materials that do not allow any transmission of light are described as ____.
a. transparent b. translucent c. opaque d. luminous

d 8. What kind of process is the mixing of primary colors of light to produce other colors?
a. refractive b. diffractive c. subtractive d. additive

For each of the statements below, write true *or rewrite the italicized part to make the statement true.*

9. **straight** The clear-edged quality of the shadow that results when you put your hand into the path of light from a flashlight illustrates that light travels in a *curved* line.

10. **true** A primary pigment reflects *two* primary colors from white light.

11. **interference of light waves** The spectrum of colors produced by an oil film on water is due to the *absorption of colors by a pigment.*

12. **perpendicular** The waves that cannot pass through a polarizing filter are those that are vibrating *parallel* to the polarizing axis.

Name ____________

16 Chapter Assessment

Understanding Concepts Part B

Answer the following questions, showing your calculations.

1. What is the frequency of light with a wavelength of 7.00×10^{-7} m? What color is the light?

$$f = \frac{c}{\lambda} = \frac{(3.00 \times 10^{8}\ \text{m/s})}{(7.00 \times 10^{-7}\ \text{m})} = 4.29 \times 10^{14}\ \text{Hz}$$

The light is red.

2. What is the illuminance, in lux, for a piece of paper on a table 3.0 m from a light source that is producing 1600 lm of luminous flux?

$$E = \frac{P}{4\pi d^2} = \frac{1600\ \text{lm}}{4\pi(3.0\ \text{m})^2} = 14\ \text{lx}$$

3. A lightbulb is 4.1 m from a surface. How much luminous flux must the bulb produce if the illuminance required is 22 lx?

$$P = E4\pi d^2 = (22\ \text{lm/m}^2)(4\pi)(4.1\ \text{m})^2 = 4.6 \times 10^{3}\ \text{lm}$$

4. What is the luminous intensity, in candelas, of a bulb with 2.00×10^{3} lm of luminous flux?

$$\text{luminous intensity} = \frac{P}{4\pi} = \frac{(2.00 \times 10^{3}\ \text{lm})}{4\pi} = 159\ \text{cd}$$

5. A sodium vapor lamp emits light waves with wavelengths of 570 nm. What is the frequency of the waves?

$$f = \frac{c}{\lambda} = \frac{(3.00 \times 10^{8}\ \text{m/s})}{(5.70 \times 10^{-7}\text{m})} = 5.26 \times 10^{14}\ \text{Hz}$$

6. What is the wavelength of light that has a frequency of 5.1×10^{14} Hz?

$$\lambda = \frac{c}{f} = \frac{(3.0 \times 10^{8}\ \text{m/s})}{(5.1 \times 10^{14}\ \text{Hz})} = 5.9 \times 10^{-7}\ \text{m}$$

Name ____________

16 Chapter Assessment

Applying Concepts

Answer the following questions, using complete sentences.

1. Define a ray and describe how rays are used to study light. What aspect of the nature of light does the ray model ignore?
A ray is a straight line that represents the path of a very narrow beam of light. Rays can be used to describe how light is reflected and refracted. The use of the ray model ignores the wave nature of light.

2. Contrast luminous flux, luminous intensity, and illuminance.
Luminous flux is the rate at which light is emitted from a source. Luminous intensity is the luminous flux that falls on 1 m^2 of a sphere with a 1-m radius. Illuminance is the amount of illumination on a surface.

3. Describe the relationship between illumination on a surface and the distance the surface is from the light source.
Illumination is inversely proportional to the square of the distance from the light source.

4. Explain why a dandelion appears yellow in white light. Is the process additive or subtractive?
When a dandelion is illuminated by white light, the molecules that make up the flower act as dyes that absorb blue light and reflect red and green light, which together are seen as yellow. The process is subtractive.

5. How is a dye different from a pigment? How are the two similar?
Dyes are molecules. Pigment particles are larger than molecules. Both dyes and pigments are colored materials that absorb certain wavelengths of light and transmit or reflect others.

6. How can you tell whether light is polarized?
A polarizing filter can be placed in the path of the light in question. If the light is already polarized, rotation of the filter will allow transmission only at certain angles. At other angles—particularly when the plane of vibration that can pass through the filter is perpendicular to the plane of the polarized light—the light will be prevented from passing through.

Name ______

16 Chapter Assessment

Answer the following questions, showing your calculations.

7. The radius of Saturn's orbit is 1.43×10^9 km. How many minutes will it take light to cross its orbit?

diameter $= 2(1.43 \times 10^9 \text{ km})$

$= 2.86 \times 10^9 \text{ km}$, or 2.86×10^{12} m

$$t = \frac{d}{v} = \frac{(2.86 \times 10^{12} \text{ m})}{(3.00 \times 10^8 \text{ m/s})} = 9.53 \times 10^3 \text{ s}$$

$$\frac{(9.53 \times 10^3 \text{ s})}{(60 \text{ s/min})} = 159 \text{ min}$$

8. One watt of electromagnetic energy produces about 500 lm of luminous flux. What is the illumination produced on a book by a fluorescent bulb that is 2.0 m from the book and that uses 40 W of electrical power? Assume that the bulb operates at 20 percent efficiency. In other words, only 0.2 of each watt of electric power provided to the bulb is converted to watts of usable electromagnetic energy in the form of light. (Hint: First calculate luminous flux, then illuminance.)

$$P = (40 \text{ W})(0.2)(500 \text{ lm/W}) = 4 \times 10^3 \text{ lm}$$

$$E = \frac{P}{4\pi d^2} = \frac{(4 \times 10^3 \text{ lm})}{4\pi(2.0 \text{ m})^2} = 80 \text{ lm/m}^2 = 80 \text{ lx}$$

9. Suppose the fluorescent bulb in problem 8 were replaced by a 40-W incandescent bulb at the same distance from the book. Calculate the book's illuminance produced by the incandescent bulb, which operates at only 3 percent efficiency.

$$P = (40 \text{ W})(0.03)(500 \text{ lm/W}) = 600 \text{ lm}$$

$$E = \frac{P}{4\pi d^2} = \frac{600 \text{ lm}}{4\pi(2.0 \text{ m})^2} = 10 \text{ lm/m}^2 = 10 \text{ lx}$$

Date ______ Period ______ Name ______

17 Chapter Assessment

Use with Chapter 17.

Reflection and Refraction

Understanding Concepts Part A

Write the letter of the choice that best completes the statement or answers the question.

b 1. From which surface would light rays undergo regular reflection?
- **a.** white construction paper
- **b.** a telescope mirror
- **c.** a piece of black cloth
- **d.** a concrete sidewalk

a 2. Refraction occurs when ____.
- **a.** light travels through two media that have different optical densities.
- **b.** light strikes the boundary of two media that have the same optical density.
- **c.** the angle of incidence equals zero.
- **d.** the angle of reflection equals zero.

a 3. When light rays travel from one medium into a less optically dense medium, ____.
- **a.** the rays speed up
- **b.** the angle of refraction is smaller than the angle of incidence
- **c.** the refracted rays bend toward the normal
- **d.** the angle of incidence equals the angle of refraction

c 4. The index of refraction of the transparent mineral beryl is approximately 1.6. Transparent quartz has an index of 1.54. Diamond has an index of 2.42. Based on these facts, which statement is true?
- **a.** All three minerals disperse light to the same extent.
- **b.** Quartz disperses light more than does beryl.
- **c.** Beryl disperses light more than does quartz.
- **d.** Both beryl and quartz disperse light more than does diamond.

For each of the statements below, write true *or rewrite the italicized part to make the statement true.*

5. **equal to** The angle of incidence is always *less than* the angle of reflection.

6. **slower** The higher the index of refraction is, the *faster* is the speed of light in the substance.

7. **true** For most practical purposes, the index of refraction of the air can be considered equal to *1.00*.

8. **smaller** A vacuum has an index of refraction that is *larger* than that of any substance.

9. **smaller** In a glass prism, the index of refraction for red light is *larger* than that for violet light.

17 Chapter Assessment

Name ______________________

Understanding Concepts Part B

Answer the following questions, showing your calculations.

1. Suppose that light rays traveling through air reach quartz at an angle of 35°. The index of refraction of quartz is 1.54. At what angle do the light rays travel within the quartz?

$$n_r \sin\theta_r = n_i \sin\theta_i$$

$$\sin\theta_r = \frac{n_i \sin\theta_i}{n_r} = \frac{(1.00)(0.574)}{1.54} = 0.373$$

$$\theta_r = 22°$$

2. A light ray enters a substance from air at an angle of 55°. The light is refracted inside the substance and travels at an angle of 35°. What is the index of refraction of the substance?

$$n_r \sin\theta_r = n_i \sin\theta_i$$

$$n_r = \frac{n_i \sin\theta_i}{\sin\theta_r} = \frac{(1.00)(0.819)}{0.574} = 1.43$$

3. Diamond has an index of refraction of 2.42. If it is immersed in water, which has an index of 1.33, and light rays in the water enter the diamond at a 53° angle, what is the angle of refraction inside the diamond?

$$n_r \sin\theta_r = n_i \sin\theta_i$$

$$\sin\theta_r = \frac{n_i \sin\theta_i}{n_r} = \frac{(1.33)(0.799)}{2.42} = 0.439$$

$$\theta_r = 26°$$

4. The index of refraction of halite, or rock salt, is 1.54. What is the speed of light in that mineral?

$$v_{halite} = \frac{c}{n_{halite}} = \frac{3.00 \times 10^8 \text{ m/s}}{1.54} = 1.95 \times 10^8 \text{ m/s}$$

17 Chapter Assessment

Name ______________________

Applying Concepts

Answer the following questions, using complete sentences.

1. Explain the difference between regular and diffuse reflection.

When light rays strike a rough surface, they reflect in many directions, causing diffuse reflection. When parallel rays of light strike a flat, very smooth surface, they reflect in parallel, causing regular reflection.

2. Explain the relationship between the sine of the angle of incidence and the sine of the angle of refraction of light rays traveling from a vacuum into a medium.

The sine of the angle of incidence divided by the sine of the angle of refraction is equal to a constant called the index of refraction of the medium.

3. Mathematically express the relationship between indices of refraction for a light ray traveling from one medium into another.

$n_i \sin\theta_i = n_r \sin\theta_r$.

4. What is total internal reflection and the critical angle?

Total internal reflection occurs when light passes from a medium into a less optically dense medium at an angle of incidence so great that no ray is refracted. The incident angle that produces a refracted ray that lies along the boundary of the two media is the critical angle.

5. How does the angle of refraction compare to the angle of incidence as a light ray passes from one medium into another with a lower index of refraction? What happens as the angle of incidence is increased?

The angle of refraction is greater than the angle of incidence. As the angle of incidence increases, the angle of refraction increases until it reaches 90°. Further increases in the angle of incidence produce total internal reflection, and there are no more refracted rays.

6. Why is the sun still visible over the horizon for a time after the actual sunset?

Sunlight travels more slowly through the air than it does in outer space. Thus, the light is refracted as it enters the atmosphere. In the evening, the sunlight is refracted so that it appears to be above the horizon when it is actually below the horizon.

Name ____________

17 Chapter Assessment

Answer the following questions, showing your calculations.

7. Flint glass has indices of refraction of 1.57 for red light and 1.59 for violet light. If an incident ray of white light moving through the air reaches the glass at an angle of 65.0°, what will the angles of refraction be for the red and the violet light components?

For the red light:

$n_r \sin\theta_r = n_i \sin\theta_i$

$\sin\theta_r = \frac{n_i \sin\theta_i}{n_r}$

$= \frac{(1.00)(0.906)}{1.57}$

$= 0.577$

$\theta_r = 35.3°$

For the violet light:

$\sin\theta_r = \frac{(1.00)(0.906)}{1.59}$

$= 0.570$

$\theta_r = 34.8°$

8. Suppose that the flint glass from problem 7 is again used to refract white light. The source of the light is adjusted so that the light reaches the glass at an angle of 60.0°. What are the angles of refraction for the two colors of light?

For the red light:

$n_r \sin\theta_r = n_i \sin\theta_i$

$\sin\theta_r = \frac{n_i \sin\theta_i}{n_r}$

$= \frac{(1.00)(0.866)}{1.57}$

$= 0.552$

$\theta_r = 33.5°$

For the violet light:

$\sin\theta_r = \frac{(1.00)(0.866)}{1.59}$

$= 0.545$

$\theta_r = 33.0°$

9. A light ray in a tub of water makes an angle of incidence of 52° as it reaches the surface from below. The index of refraction of air is 1.00 and that of water is 1.33.

a. Show that the ray undergoes total internal reflection.

$n_{air} \sin\theta_r = n_{water} \sin\theta_i$

$\sin\theta_r = \frac{n_{water} \sin\theta_i}{n_{air}}$

$= \frac{(1.33)(0.788)}{1.00}$

$= 1.05$

No angle produces a sine value greater than 1, so there is no refracted ray. Total internal reflection must therefore occur.

b. What is the value of the angle of reflection for the reflected ray?

By the law of reflection, the angle of reflection equals the angle of incidence, 52°.

Date ____________ Period ____________ Name ____________

18 Chapter Assessment

Use with Chapter 18.

Mirrors and Lenses

Understanding Concepts Part A

Write the letter of the choice that best completes the statement or answers the question.

c 1. The focal length of a spherical mirror equals ____.
- **a.** the radius of curvature
- **b.** twice the radius of curvature
- **c.** half the radius of curvature
- **d.** half the length of the principal axis

b 2. When a real image is formed, ____.
- **a.** light rays seem to diverge behind the mirror
- **b.** light rays converge at the image
- **c.** the image cannot be projected on a screen
- **d.** the image is always inverted

d 3. If an object is between a concave mirror and its focal point, the image will be ____.
- **a.** real and smaller than the object
- **b.** real and larger than the object
- **c.** virtual and smaller than the object
- **d.** virtual and larger than the object

a 4. The image formed of an object located more than twice the focal length from a convex lens is ____.
- **a.** real and smaller than the object
- **b.** real and larger than the object
- **c.** virtual and smaller than the object
- **d.** virtual and larger than the object

For each of the statements below, write true *or rewrite the italicized part to make the statement true.*

5. **true** — *Chromatic* aberration can be reduced by joining together a converging lens and a diverging lens.

6. **negative** — Concave lenses have *positive* focal lengths.

7. **telescopes** — Parabolic mirrors are often used in *microscopes*.

8. **true** — Rays parallel to the principal axis of a *concave* mirror converge at the focal point.

9. **true** — *Magnification* is equal to the size of the image divided by the size of the object.

Name ______________________

18 Chapter Assessment

Understanding Concepts Part B

1. A thimble is 32.0 cm from a concave mirror. The focal point of the mirror is 11.0 cm. Where is the image located?

$$\frac{1}{f} = \frac{1}{d_o} + \frac{1}{d_i}$$

$$d_i = \frac{fd_o}{d_o - f}$$

$$= \frac{(11.0\ \text{cm})(32.0\ \text{cm})}{(32.0\ \text{cm}) - (11.0\ \text{cm})}$$

= 16.8 cm from the mirror

2. What are the size and orientation of the image of the thimble from problem 1 if the thimble itself is 2.50 cm tall?

$$\frac{h_i}{h_o} = \frac{-d_i}{d_o}$$

$$h_i = \frac{-h_o d_i}{d_o}$$

$$= \frac{-(2.50\ \text{cm})(16.8\ \text{cm})}{32.0\ \text{cm}}$$

$$= -1.31\ \text{cm}$$

The negative sign indicates that the image is inverted.

3. What is the magnification in problem 2?

$$m = \frac{h_i}{h_o}$$

$$= \frac{-1.31\ \text{cm}}{2.50\ \text{cm}}$$

$$= -0.524$$

4. A child who is 1.1 m tall is standing 6.0 m from a concave mirror. The child's image is 0.40 m behind the mirror. What is the size of the image?

$$\frac{h_i}{h_o} = \frac{-d_i}{d_o}$$

$$h_i = \frac{-h_o d_i}{d_o}$$

$$= \frac{-(1.1\ \text{m})(-0.40\ \text{m})}{6.0\ \text{cm}}$$

$$= 0.073\ \text{m}$$

Name ______________________

18 Chapter Assessment

5. What is the focal length of the mirror in problem 4?

$$\frac{1}{f} = \frac{1}{d_o} + \frac{1}{d_i}$$

$$f = \frac{d_i d_o}{d_i + d_o}$$

$$= \frac{(6.0\ \text{m})(-0.40\ \text{m})}{(6.0\ \text{m}) + (-0.40\ \text{m})}$$

$$= -0.43\ \text{m}$$

6. An object is 5.00 cm from a convex lens that has a focal length of 6.00 cm. Locate the image and determine whether it is real or virtual.

$$\frac{1}{f} = \frac{1}{d_o} + \frac{1}{d_i}$$

$$d_i = \frac{fd_o}{d_o - f}$$

$$= \frac{(6.00\ \text{cm})(5.00\ \text{cm})}{(5.00\ \text{cm}) - (6.00\ \text{cm})}$$

$$= -30.0\ \text{cm}$$

The negative sign indicates that the image is virtual.

7. What is the focal length of a concave lens that forms an image with a d_i value of −10.0 cm when an object is 35.0 cm from the lens?

$$\frac{1}{f} = \frac{1}{d_o} + \frac{1}{d_i}$$

$$f = \frac{d_i d_o}{d_i + d_o}$$

$$= \frac{(-10.0\ \text{cm})(35.0\ \text{cm})}{(-10.0\ \text{cm}) + (35.0\ \text{cm})}$$

$$= -14.0\ \text{cm}$$

Name ______________

18 Chapter Assessment

Applying Concepts

Answer the following questions, using complete sentences.

1. What happens to a light ray that enters parallel to the principal axis of a concave mirror? What happens to a ray that passes through the focal point of such a mirror before being reflected?
   A ray that is parallel to the principal axis passes through the focal point of a concave mirror. A ray that passes through the focal point of the mirror is reflected parallel to the principal axis.

2. Explain what causes spherical aberration.
   Rays parallel to the principal axis converge at the focal point of a spherical mirror only if the rays are close to the principal axis. Rays far from the principal axis converge at points closer to the mirror's surface. Thus, the image formed in a large spherical mirror is a disk rather than a point.

3. Contrast convex and concave lenses.
   A convex lens is thicker at the center than it is at the edges and refracts light rays that are parallel to the principal axis so that they converge. A concave lens is thinner in the center than at the edges and refracts light rays so that they diverge.

4. Contrast the image formed by a converging lens when an object is located more than twice the focal length from the lens, with the image formed when the object is between the lens and the focus.
   If the object is more than twice the focal length away, the image is real, inverted, and reduced. If the object is between the focus and the lens, the image is virtual, erect, and enlarged.

5. Contrast concave and convex mirrors.
   Both kinds of mirrors are curved. The reflective surface of a concave mirror is curved inward, that of a convex mirror is curved outward. Light rays that enter parallel to the principal axis of a concave mirror go through the focal point. Objects that are much farther out than the focal point produce real, inverted, reduced images. Objects between the focal point and the mirror produce virtual, erect, enlarged images. Convex mirrors always produce images that are virtual, erect, and reduced.

6. Explain the operation of mirrors used in stores to observe shoppers.
   The mirrors are large and convex. Because they are convex, they produce reduced virtual images but reflect an enlarged field of view, allowing a large area of the store to be visible in the mirror.

Name ______________

18 Chapter Assessment

Answer the following questions, showing your calculations.

7. You want to create a 0.035-m image of a flower that is 1.00 m high and 10.0 m from a concave mirror. What must the radius of curvature of the mirror be?

$$\frac{-d_i}{d_o} = \frac{h_i}{h_o}$$

$$d_i = \frac{-d_o h_i}{h_o} = \frac{-(10.0\ \text{m})(-0.035\ \text{m})}{1.00\ \text{m}} = 0.35\ \text{m}$$

$$\frac{1}{f} = \frac{1}{d_o} + \frac{1}{d_i}$$

$$f = \frac{d_i d_o}{d_i + d_o} = \frac{(10.0\ \text{m})(0.35\ \text{m})}{(10.0\ \text{m}) + (0.35\ \text{m})} = 0.34\ \text{m}$$

$$r = 2f = 2(0.34\ \text{m}) = 0.68\ \text{m}$$

8. If a vehicle 2.0 m high is 4.6 m from a car's convex mirror, find the position and size of the image, given that the radius of curvature is 0.80 m. Is the image real or virtual? Is it erect or inverted? Give reasons for your answer.

$$f = \frac{-r}{2} = \frac{-0.80\ \text{m}}{2} = -0.40\ \text{m}$$

$$\frac{1}{f} = \frac{1}{d_o} + \frac{1}{d_i}$$

$$d_i = \frac{f d_o}{d_o - f} = \frac{(-0.40\ \text{m})(4.6\ \text{m})}{(4.6\ \text{m}) - (-0.40\ \text{m})} = -0.37\ \text{m}$$

The negative value indicates a virtual image.

$$\frac{h_i}{h_o} = \frac{-d_i}{d_o}$$

$$h_i = \frac{-h_o d_i}{d_o} = \frac{-(2.0\ \text{m})(-0.37\ \text{m})}{4.6\ \text{m}} = 0.16\ \text{m}$$

The positive value indicates an erect image.

Name ______

18 Chapter Assessment

9. A object that is 0.95 cm tall and 4.2 cm from a convex lens produces a real image that is 2.8 cm from the other side of the lens.

a. What is the size of the image? Is the image erect or inverted? Is the image enlarged or reduced?

$$\frac{h_i}{h_o} = \frac{-d_i}{d_o}$$

$$h_i = \frac{-h_o d_i}{d_o}$$

$$= \frac{-(0.95\text{ cm})(2.8\text{ cm})}{4.2\text{ cm}}$$

$$= -0.63\text{ cm}$$

The negative value indicates an inverted image. Because the absolute value of h_i is less than that of h_o, the image is reduced.

b. What is the magnification of the lens? What is the focal length of the lens?

$$m = \frac{h_i}{h_o}$$

$$= \frac{-0.63\text{ cm}}{0.95\text{ cm}}$$

$$= -0.66$$

$$\frac{1}{f} = \frac{1}{d_o} + \frac{1}{d_i}$$

$$f = \frac{d_i d_o}{d_i + d_o}$$

$$= \frac{(2.8\text{ cm})(4.2\text{ cm})}{(2.8\text{ cm}) + (4.2\text{ cm})}$$

$$= 1.7\text{ cm}$$

Date ______ Period ______ Name ______

19 Chapter Assessment

Use with Chapter 19.

Diffraction and Interference of Light

Understanding Concepts Part A

Write the letter of the choice that best completes the statement or answers the question.

b 1. The destructive and constructive interference of light that passes through two closely spaced slits produces ____.
- a. a single continuous spectrum
- b. interference fringes
- c. a continuous white band
- d. a single band of one color

a 2. The bending of waves around the edges of barriers is called ____.
- a. diffraction
- b. refraction
- c. reflection
- d. dispersion

b 3. The paths of light waves that come from two slits and that interfere to form first-order lines ____.
- a. are exactly the same length
- b. differ in length by the wavelength of the light
- c. are parallel
- d. are perpendicular

c 4. When light passes through a single slit, which of the following appears?
- a. a series of equally bright bands
- b. a dark central band, with bright bands to the sides
- c. a bright central band, with dimmer bands to the sides
- d. a single wide bright band

d 5. A pair of closely spaced stars can be seen as a single star because a telescope lens has limited ____.
- a. index of refraction
- b. chromatic aberration
- c. reflective ability
- d. resolving power

a 6. The effects of diffraction on the ability of telescopes to distinguish between closely spaced stars can be reduced by ____.
- a. increasing the size of the lens
- b. decreasing the size of the lens
- c. using red filters
- d. reducing the amount of light entering the telescope

For each of the statements below, write true *or rewrite the italicized part to make the statement true.*

7. **true** Diffraction is *more obvious* for sound waves than for light waves.

8. **true** For a *single-slit* experiment, the distance x is equal to $\lambda L/w$.

9. ***d*** The symbol used to represent the distance between two slits is *L*.

10. ***xd/L*** For a two-slit experiment, the wavelength equals $\lambda d/L$.

Name ______________

19 Chapter Assessment

Understanding Concepts Part B

Answer the following questions, showing your calculations.

1. Suppose the separation between two slits is 1.72×10^{-5} m and the screen is 0.650 m from the slits. If monochromatic violet light with a wavelength of 4.50×10^{-7} m passes through the slits, how far from the central band will the first band of the violet light appear?

$$x = \frac{\lambda L}{d} = \frac{(4.50 \times 10^{-7}\ \text{m})(0.650\ \text{m})}{1.72 \times 10^{-5}\ \text{m}} = 1.70 \times 10^{-2}\ \text{m}$$

2. A red laser beam falls on two slits that are 1.95×10^{-5} m apart. A first-order line appears 4.42×10^{-2} m from the central bright line. If the screen is 1.25 m from the slits, what is the wavelength of the light?

$$\lambda = \frac{xd}{L} = \frac{(4.42 \times 10^{-2}\ \text{m})(1.95 \times 10^{-5}\ \text{m})}{1.25\ \text{m}} = 6.90 \times 10^{-7}\ \text{m}$$

3. Suppose that monochromatic light that has a wavelength of 570 nm passes through two slits that are separated by 1.90×10^{-5} m and that are 0.800 m from the screen. What is the distance from the central line to the first-order line?

$$x = \frac{\lambda L}{d} = \frac{(5.70 \times 10^{-7}\ \text{m})(0.800\ \text{m})}{1.90 \times 10^{-5}\ \text{m}} = 0.0240\ \text{m}$$

Name ______________

19 Chapter Assessment

4. Suppose that the double slit in problem 3 is replaced by a single slit 0.0900 mm wide. What is the distance from the center of the central band to the first dark band?

$$x = \frac{\lambda L}{w} = \frac{(5.70 \times 10^{-7}\ \text{m})(0.800\ \text{m})}{9.00 \times 10^{-5}\ \text{m}} = 5.07 \times 10^{-3}\ \text{m}$$

5. Suppose that a diffraction grating has 6.00×10^{3} lines per centimeter. The screen is 0.400 m from the grating. If monochromatic light shines on the grating, and the first-order line appears on the screen 12.9 cm from the central line, what is the wavelength of the light?

$$d = \frac{1\ \text{cm}}{6.00 \times 10^{3}} = 1.67 \times 10^{-4}\ \text{cm} = 1.67 \times 10^{-6}\ \text{m}$$

$$\lambda = \frac{xd}{L} = \frac{(1.29 \times 10^{-1}\ \text{m})(1.67 \times 10^{-6}\ \text{m})}{0.400\ \text{m}} = 5.39 \times 10^{-7}\ \text{m} = 539\ \text{nm}$$

Name ______________________

19 Chapter Assessment

Applying Concepts

Answer the following questions, using complete sentences

1. Why are the edges of shadows not perfectly sharp? What is this phenomenon called?
The bending of light waves around the edges of barriers causes the fuzzy edges of shadows. This bending phenomenon is diffraction.

2. Why did diffraction suggest that the corpuscular model of light is not entirely correct? What experiment first measured wavelengths of light?
A wave model worked better to explain diffraction. The two-slit experiment allowed for precise measurement of light's wavelength, using diffraction.

3. Explain how single-slit diffraction causes dark bands.
No light is seen when the paths of two light waves differ in length by $\lambda/2$ or multiples of $\lambda/2$ because destructive interference occurs.

4. Compare the diffraction of light and sound, and account for any differences.
Both light and sound are diffracted. The degree of diffraction depends upon wavelength, and because sound has much longer wavelengths, it is diffracted much more noticeably than light.

5. Contrast the interference patterns formed by double slits with those formed by diffraction gratings.
The patterns are formed in the same way. Bright bands are in the same locations, but are narrower when formed by diffraction gratings. The dark regions formed by gratings are broader than those formed by double slits. The colors produced by the gratings are also more easily distinguished, and wavelengths can be measured more precisely with diffraction gratings.

6. Can the values for the wavelengths of the components of white light be measured directly with a grating spectrometer? Give a reason for your answer.
Wavelengths cannot be measured directly, but can be calculated. When white light falls on a slit and reaches a diffraction grating, a series of bright bands appears on either side of the central bright band. The spectrometer telescope is moved until the desired line appears in the middle of a viewer. The angle θ is directly read from the spectrometer. If you know the value of d, you can calculate the wavelength, $d \sin \theta$.

Name ______________________

19 Chapter Assessment

Answer the following questions, showing your calculations.

7. The range of wavelengths for visible light is about 400–700 nm. At what angle will the first-order line for violet light of wavelength 400 nm be produced by a diffraction grating that has 1.00×10^4 lines per centimeter?

$$d = \frac{1 \text{ cm}}{1.00 \times 10^4}$$
$$= 1.00 \times 10^{-4} \text{ cm} = 1.00 \times 10^{-6} \text{ m}$$
$$\sin \theta = \frac{\lambda}{d} = \frac{4.00 \times 10^{-7} \text{ m}}{1.00 \times 10^{-6} \text{ m}} = 0.400$$
$$\theta = 23.6°$$

8. At what angle will the first-order line for red light of wavelength 700 nm be produced by the diffraction grating in problem 7?

$$\sin \theta = \frac{\lambda}{d} = \frac{7.00 \times 10^{-7} \text{ m}}{(1.00 \times 10^{-6} \text{ m})} = 0.700$$
$$\theta = 44.4°$$

9. When white light shines on it, a diffraction grating forms a number of spectra on either side of the central band. The spectra can be assigned a number corresponding to their order. The symbol for this order number is m ($m = 1$ for first order, etc.). The equation $\sin \theta = m\lambda/d$ gives the angle for light that appears in a spectral band of order m. Apply this equation to find the angle for the third-order violet light that has a wavelength of 400 nm. The lines on the diffraction grating are 1.00×10^{-5} m apart.

$$\sin \theta = \frac{m\lambda}{d} = \frac{3(4.00 \times 10^{-7} \text{ m})}{1.00 \times 10^{-5} \text{ m}} = 0.120$$
$$\theta = 6.89°$$

Name ____________

19 Chapter Assessment

10. Using the same procedure as in problem 9, find the angle for the second-order red light that has a wavelength of 700 nm, using the same grating. Compare the angle to the one calculated in problem 9. What can you conclude about these second- and third-order spectral bands, in terms of overlap?

$$\sin\theta = \frac{m\lambda}{d}$$

$$= \frac{2(7.00 \times 10^{-7}\ \text{m})}{1.00 \times 10^{-5}\ \text{m}}$$

$$= 0.140$$

$$\theta = 8.05^\circ$$

The angle for the second-order red is greater than that for the third-order violet, so the spectral bands must overlap.

11. Rearrange the equation $\sin\theta = m\lambda/d$ to find the upper limit for observable wavelength that can be observed in the fourth order for a diffraction grating that has 5.00×10^3 lines per centimeter. Note that the angle for the longest observable wavelength cannot exceed 90°.

$$d = \frac{1\ \text{cm}}{5.00 \times 10^3}$$

$$= 2.00 \times 10^{-4}\ \text{cm} = 2.00 \times 10^{-6}\ \text{m}$$

$$\lambda = \frac{d(\sin\theta)}{m}$$

$$= \frac{(2.00 \times 10^{-6}\ \text{m})(\sin 90^\circ)}{4}$$

$$= 5.00 \times 10^{-7}\ \text{m} = 500\ \text{nm}$$

Date ____________ Period ____________ Name ____________

20 Chapter Assessment

Use with Chapter 20.

Static Electricity

Understanding Concepts Part A

For each of the statements below, write true or rewrite the italicized part to make the statement true.

1. **true** Bits of paper stick to a plastic comb that has been rubbed because of *electric charge.*
2. **true** When electrons are transferred from one object to another, positive and negative charges are *separated.*
3. **insulators** Charges in *conductors* cannot easily move around.
4. **cannot** Coulomb's law *can* be used to find magnitude and the direction of an electric force between two charged objects.
5. **conduction** Touching an electroscope with a negatively charged rod is an example of charging by *induction.*

Write the letter of the choice that best completes the statement or answers the question.

b 6. When an electroscope is charged, its leaves spread apart because ____.
- a. unlike charges repel
- b. charges exert force on other charges over a distance
- c. positive charges spread over the metal surfaces
- d. negative charges spread over the metal surfaces

c 7. The force that charge q_A exerts on charge q_B is opposite and ____ the force that charge q_B exerts on q_A.
- a. greater than
- b. less than
- c. equal to

a 8. Electric force is a vector quantity because it has magnitude and ____.
- a. direction
- b. duration
- c. frequency
- d. strength

b 9. If an electroscope that is negatively charged is touched with a rod with a negative charge, ____.
- a. there will be no effect
- b. the leaves will spread farther apart
- c. the leaves will fall
- d. the electroscope will become positively charged

Name ____________

20 Chapter Assessment

Understanding Concepts Part B

Answer the following questions, showing your calculations.

1. Assuming the force exerted between two spheres is 64 N, what will be the magnitude of the force if the distance is doubled? Tripled?

   $\frac{64\ \text{N}}{4} = 16\ \text{N}$, **if double distance**

   $\frac{64\ \text{N}}{9} = 7.1\ \text{N}$, **if triple distance**

2. A positive charge of 3.6×10^{-5} C and a negative charge of -2.4×10^{-5} C are 0.034 m apart. What is the force between the two particles?

   $$F = \frac{Kq_Aq_B}{d^2}$$
   $$= \frac{(9.0 \times 10^9\ \text{N}\cdot\text{m}^2/\text{C}^2)(3.6 \times 10^{-5}\ \text{C})(2.4 \times 10^{-5}\ \text{C})}{(0.034\ \text{m})^2}$$
   $$= 6.7 \times 10^3\ \text{N}$$

3. The force between two objects is 64 N. One object has a positive charge of 1.4×10^{-6} C, while the other has a negative charge of 1.8×10^{-6} C. How far apart are the two objects?

   $$d = \sqrt{\frac{Kq_Aq_B}{F}}$$
   $$= \sqrt{\frac{(9.0 \times 10^9\ \text{N}\cdot\text{m}^2/\text{C}^2)(1.4 \times 10^{-6}\ \text{C})(1.8 \times 10^{-6}\ \text{C})}{64\ \text{N}}}$$
   $$= 1.9 \times 10^{-2}\ \text{m}$$

Name ____________

20 Chapter Assessment

4. Two negative charges of 4.2×10^{-8} C are separated by 0.46 m. What is the magnitude of the force acting on each object?

   $$F = \frac{Kq_Aq_B}{d^2}$$
   $$= \frac{(9.0 \times 10^9\ \text{N}\cdot\text{m}^2/\text{C}^2)(4.2 \times 10^{-8}\ \text{C})(4.2 \times 10^{-8}\ \text{C})}{(0.46\ \text{m})^2}$$
   $$= 7.5 \times 10^{-5}\ \text{N}$$

5. Two objects exert a force of 4.2 N on each other. The distance between the objects is 0.36 m. The charge on one object is 2.8×10^{-9} C. What is the charge on the second object?

   $$q_B = \frac{Fd^2}{Kq_A}$$
   $$= \frac{(4.2\ \text{N})(0.36\ \text{m})^2}{(9.0 \times 10^9\ \text{N}\cdot\text{m}^2/\text{C}^2)(2.8 \times 10^{-9}\ \text{C})}$$
   $$= 0.022\ \text{C}$$

Name ______________________

20 Chapter Assessment

Applying Concepts

Answer the following questions, using complete sentences.

1. Which of the following would you use to prevent the spread of an electric charge: copper, plastic, or graphite? Explain your answer.
Plastic would be used because it is a good insulator. Copper and graphite are conductors. Because charges do not move easily through insulators, they can be used to prevent the spread of electric charge.

2. Explain how objects can become charged when individual charges cannot be created or destroyed.
Charging of objects is the result of isolating positive and negative charges that already exist.

3. Why do socks and other pieces of clothing stick together after being tumbled in a dryer?
As clothing is tumbled in the hot, dry air of a dryer, electrons are pulled off the atoms in some articles of clothing and added to the atoms in others. Clothing pieces with a net negative charge are then attracted to pieces with a net positive charge.

4. Distinguish between charging by conduction and charging by induction.
In charging by conduction, electrons are transferred from one object to another by touching. In charging by induction, charges are redistributed within an object without direct contact between two objects.

5. Does charging by induction or conduction occur during a thunderstorm? Explain.
During a thunderstorm, charging by induction occurs. The bottoms of the clouds are negatively charged. They cause charge separation on Earth, and Earth's surface becomes positively charged. The cloud and Earth do not touch.

6. Two positive charges are located 2 cm apart. Charge q_A is 2×10^{-9} C and charge q_B is 3×10^{-9} C. Is the force between these charges attractive or repulsive? Explain your answer.
There is a repulsive force between the charges because they are both positive.

Name ______________________

20 Chapter Assessment

Answer the following questions, showing your calculations.

7. Two objects, one having twice the charge of the other, are separated by 0.78 m and exert a force of 3.8×10^3 N. What is the magnitude of charge on each object?

$$F = \frac{Kq(2q)}{d^2}$$

$$q = \sqrt{\frac{Fd^2}{2K}}$$

$$= \sqrt{\frac{(3.8 \times 10^3\ \text{N})(0.78\ \text{m})^2}{2(9.0 \times 10^9\ \text{N} \cdot \text{m}^2/\text{C}^2)}}$$

$$= 3.6 \times 10^{-4}\ \text{C}$$

$$2q = 2(3.6 \times 10^{-4}\ \text{C}) = 7.2 \times 10^{-4}\ \text{C}$$

The charges on the two objects are 3.6×10^{-4} C and 7.2×10^{-4} C.

8. The drawing below shows the charges on three objects and the distances between them. Charges A and C are 90° apart with respect to charge B. Calculate the magnitude of the net charge acting on charge B.

A: -4.2×10^{-5} C
0.060 m
B: 8.4×10^{-5} C
0.140 m
C: 2.1×10^{-5} C

$$F = \frac{Kq_Aq_B}{d^2}$$

$$F_{AonB} = \frac{(9.0 \times 10^9\ \text{N} \cdot \text{m}^2/\text{C}^2)(8.4 \times 10^{-5}\ \text{C})(4.2 \times 10^{-5}\ \text{C})}{(6.0 \times 10^{-2}\ \text{m})^2}$$

$$= 8.8 \times 10^3\ \text{N}$$

$$F_{ConB} = \frac{(9.0 \times 10^9\ \text{N} \cdot \text{m}^2/\text{C}^2)(8.4 \times 10^{-5}\ \text{C})(2.1 \times 10^{-5}\ \text{C})}{(1.4 \times 10^{-1}\ \text{m})^2}$$

$$= 8.1 \times 10^2\ \text{N}$$

$$F_{net} = \sqrt{(8.8 \times 10^3\ \text{N})^2 + (8.1 \times 10^2\ \text{N})^2}$$

$$= 8.8 \times 10^3\ \text{N}$$

Name ____________________

20 Chapter Assessment

9. Draw a diagram of the force vectors of A on B and C on B. What is the vector angle of the net force acting on charge B? Add this vector to your drawing, showing its approximate position.

$$\tan\theta = \frac{\text{opposite}}{\text{adjacent}} = \frac{8.8 \times 10^3\ \text{N}}{8.1 \times 10^2\ \text{N}} = 10.9$$

$\theta = 85°$

F_T F_1

θ

F_2

Date ____________ Period ____________ Name ____________________

21 Chapter Assessment

Use with Chapter 21.

Electric Fields

Understanding Concepts Part A

Write the letter of the choice that best completes each statement.

b 1. An electric field is equal to _____.
- a. force per unit mass
- b. force per unit charge
- c. force per unit time
- d. force times direction

a 2. The force on a test charge in an electric field is _____.
- a. directly proportional to the magnitude of the field
- b. inversely proportional to the magnitude of the field
- c. inversely proportional to the square of the magnitude of the field
- d. unrelated to the magnitude of the field

d 3. The strength of the force on a charge in an electric field depends on _____.
- a. the direction of the field
- b. the magnitude of the field
- c. the size of the charge
- d. both the magnitude of the field and the size of the charge

c 4. As an electric field becomes stronger, the field lines should be drawn _____.
- a. thicker
- b. thinner
- c. closer together
- d. farther apart

d 5. A good device to indicate electric field lines is _____.
- a. a Leyden jar
- b. a capacitor
- c. a lightning rod
- d. a Van de Graaff machine

For each of the statements below, write true *or rewrite the italicized part to make the statement true.*

6. **unlike** With two *like* charges, you must do work to pull one charge away from the other.

7. **true** In a *uniform electric field,* the potential difference between two points is found using the equation $\Delta V = Ed$.

8. **electron** Robert Millikan determined that the charge of a *proton* is 1.6×10^{-19} C.

9. **true** Touching an object to Earth to eliminate excess charge is *grounding*.

10. **outer** The charges on a hollow conductor are found on the *inner* surface.

11. **true** A *capacitor* is made up of two conductors separated by an insulator.

Name ______________

21 Chapter Assessment

Understanding Concepts Part B

1. A force of 0.43 N acts on a positive charge of 2.4×10^{-6} C at a certain distance. What is the electric field intensity at that distance?

$$E = \frac{F}{q} = \frac{4.3 \times 10^{-1}\ \text{N}}{2.4 \times 10^{-6}\ \text{C}} = 1.8 \times 10^{5}\ \text{N/C}$$

2. What charge does a test charge have when a force of 3.60×10^{-6} N acts on it at a point where the electric field intensity is 1.60×10^{-5} N/C?

$$q = \frac{F}{E} = \frac{3.60 \times 10^{-6}\ \text{N}}{1.60 \times 10^{-5}\ \text{N/C}} = 0.225\ \text{C}$$

3. The electric field intensity between two charged plates is 2.80×10^{4} N/C. The plates are 0.0640 m apart. What is the potential difference between the plates in volts?

$$\Delta V = Ed = (2.80 \times 10^{4}\ \text{N/C})(0.0640\ \text{m}) = 1.79 \times 10^{3}\ \text{V}$$

4. A voltmeter connected between two plates registers 38.2 V. The plates are separated by a distance of 0.046 m. What is the field intensity between the plates?

$$E = \frac{\Delta V}{d} = \frac{38.2\ \text{V}}{0.046\ \text{m}} = 830\ \text{V/m} = 830\ \text{N/C}$$

5. How much work is done to transfer 0.47 C of charge through a potential difference of 12 V?

$$W = q\Delta V = (0.47\ \text{C})(12\ \text{V}) = 5.6\ \text{J}$$

6. A 9.0-V battery does 1.0×10^{3} J of work transferring charge. How much charge is transferred?

$$q = \frac{W}{\Delta V} = \frac{1.0 \times 10^{3}\ \text{J}}{9.0\ \text{V}} = 1.1 \times 10^{2}\ \text{C}$$

Name ______________

21 Chapter Assessment

Applying Concepts

Answer the following questions, using complete sentences.

1. Compare an electric field to a gravitational field.
Both an electric field and a gravitational field act between bodies that are not in contact with each other. In a gravitational field, one mass exerts a force on another mass. In an electric field, one charge exerts a force on another charge. An electric field is the force per unit charge. A gravitational field is the force per unit mass.

2. What is the direction of an electric field between a negative and a positive charge?
The field is away from the positive charge and toward the negative charge.

3. Explain why electric potential energy is larger when two like charges are close together than when two unlike charges are close together.
Since like charges repel each other, more work is done in bringing them together than in bringing together unlike charges.

4. If a high-voltage wire falls on a car, will the people inside be safe from electrocution? Explain your answer.
Yes. The car is a closed metal conductor that is hollow. Charges move to the external surface, shielding the interior from the electric field.

5. What is the net charge on a capacitor? Explain your answer.
The net charge is zero since the two conductors have equal and opposite charge.

Name ____________

21 Chapter Assessment

Answer the following questions, showing your calculations.

6. A force of 7.60×10^3 N acts on a charge of 1.60×10^{-2} C in a uniform field over a distance of 0.0440 m. What is the potential difference of this system?

$\Delta V = Ed \qquad E = \frac{F}{q}$

$\Delta V = \frac{Fd}{q}$

$= \frac{(7.60 \times 10^3\ \text{N})(0.0440\ \text{m})}{1.60 \times 10^{-2}\ \text{C}}$

$= 2.09 \times 10^4\ \text{V}$

7. How much work is done by a system in which the force is 6.8×10^4 N, the potential difference is 4.2 V, and the electric field intensity is 1.2×10^{-3} N/C?

$W = q\Delta V \qquad q = \frac{F}{E}$

$W = \frac{F\Delta V}{E}$

$= \frac{(6.8 \times 10^4\ \text{N})(4.2\ \text{V})}{1.2 \times 10^{-3}\ \text{N/C}}$

$= 2.4 \times 10^8\ \text{J}$

8. How much energy is stored in a capacitor of 12.2 μF that has been charged to 4.26×10^2 V?

$\Delta PE = W \qquad W = q\Delta V \qquad q = C\Delta V$

$W = C\Delta V^2$

$= (1.22 \times 10^{-5}\ \text{F})(4.26 \times 10^2\ \text{V})^2$

$= 2.21\ \text{J}$

9. How much power is required to charge a capacitor of 9.4 μF to 5.4×10^2 V in 48 s?

$P = \frac{W}{t} \qquad W = C\Delta V^2$

$P = \frac{C\Delta V^2}{t}$

$= (9.4 \times 10^{-6}\ \text{F})(5.4 \times 10^2\ \text{V})^2$

$= 5.7 \times 10^{-2}\ \text{W}$

Date ________ Period ________ Name ____________

22 Chapter Assessment

Use with Chapter 22.

Current Electricity

Understanding Concepts Part A

Use each of the following terms once to complete the statements below.

ampere	electric current	potential difference	resistance
electric circuit	kinetic energy	power	

1. **electric current** A charge pump creates a flow of charged particles, or ____.
2. **electric circuit** A closed loop through which charges can flow is a(n) ____.
3. **kinetic energy** When a water wheel drives a generator, the generator converts the ____ of the water to electric energy.
4. **power** The rate at which energy is transferred is ____.
5. **ampere** The unit used to measure the rate of flow of electric current is a(n) ____.
6. **resistance** The ____ of a conductor can be determined if potential difference and current are known.
7. **potential difference** A device that has constant resistance and appears to be independent of the ____ is said to obey Ohm's law.

Write the letter of the choice that best completes each statement.

a 8. The current flowing in an electric circuit can be increased by ____.
- a. increasing voltage or decreasing resistance
- b. decreasing voltage or increasing resistance
- c. increasing voltage and increasing resistance
- d. decreasing voltage and decreasing resistance

d 9. A device that measures the amount of current in a circuit is a(n) ____.
a. potentiometer b. resistor c. voltmeter d. ammeter

b 10. Space heaters convert most of the electric energy in a circuit into ____ energy.
a. light b. thermal c. mechanical d. sound

a 11. Electricity is carried long distances at high voltages because ____.
- a. this reduces the current and less power is lost as thermal energy
- b. this reduces the resistance and less power is lost as thermal energy
- c. current cannot be changed to reduce thermal energy
- d. capacitance cannot be changed to reduce thermal energy.

b 12. Utility companies measure energy used in ____.
a. joules b. kilowatt-hours c. watt-seconds d. watts

Name ______________

22 Chapter Assessment

Understanding Concepts Part B

Answer each of the following questions, showing your calculations.

1. A portable compact-disk player receives its energy from a 9.0-V cell. The current used to operate the player is 135 A.

   a. How many joules of energy does the cell deliver to the CD player each second?
   $P = IV$
   $= (135\ \text{A})(9.0\ \text{V})$
   $= 1.2 \times 10^3\ \text{J/s}$

   b. How much power in watts does the CD player use?
   $P = 1.2 \times 10^3\ \text{W}$

   c. How much energy does the CD player use to play a selection 3.0 min long?
   $E = Pt$
   $= (1.2 \times 10^3\ \text{J/s})(3.0\ \text{min})(60\ \text{s/min})$
   $= 2.2 \times 10^5\ \text{J}$

2. What voltage is applied to a 6.80-Ω resistor if the current is 3.20 A?
   $V = IR$
   $= (3.20\ \text{A})(6.80\ \Omega)$
   $= 21.8\ \text{V}$

3. An electric buzzer is connected across a 4.2-V difference in potential. The current through the buzzer is 1.8 A.

   a. What is the power rating of the buzzer?
   $P = IV$
   $= (1.8\ \text{A})(4.2\ \text{V})$
   $= 7.6\ \text{W}$

   b. How much electric energy does the buzzer convert in 1.5 min?
   $E = Pt$
   $= (7.6\ \text{W})(1.5\ \text{min})(60\ \text{s/min})$
   $= 680\ \text{J}$

4. An electric blanket with a resistance of 8.6 Ω is connected to a 120-V source.

   a. What is the current in the circuit?
   $I = \frac{V}{R} = \frac{120\ \text{V}}{8.6\ \Omega} = 14\ \text{A}$

   b. How much heat is produced if the blanket is turned on for 15 min?
   $E = I^2Rt$
   $= (14\ \text{A})^2(8.6\ \Omega)(15\ \text{min})(60\ \text{s/min})$
   $= 1.5 \times 10^6\ \text{J}$

Name ______________

22 Chapter Assessment

Applying Concepts

Answer the following sentences, using complete sentences.

1. What is the difference between an ampere and a volt?
   An ampere is the rate of flow of electric charge, or charge per unit of time. A volt is a measure of the voltage, or potential difference, between charges.

2. Identify the parts of this schematic. Will current flow through the circuit? Give a reason for your answer.

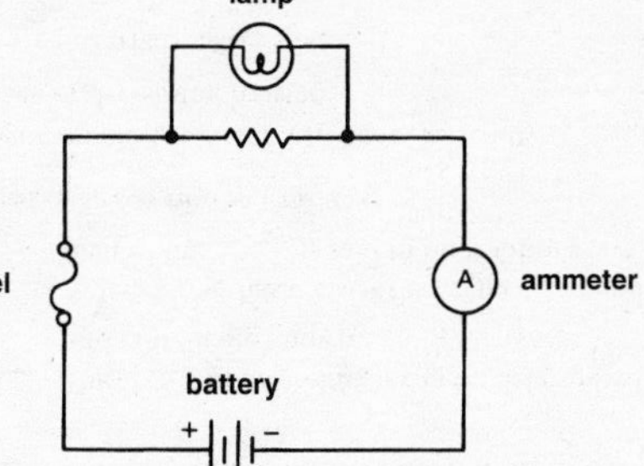

   Current will flow because the circuit forms a closed loop.

3. Could a voltmeter be substituted for the ammeter shown in the schematic in problem 2? Give a reason for your answer.
   No, the ammeter cannot be replaced by a voltmeter. The ammeter is connected in series. The voltmeter must be connected in parallel.

4. What would happen to current if voltage and resistance were doubled?
   The current would remain the same.

5. Which has a greater effect on the amount of thermal energy produced in a heater, the current or the resistance of the heater? Give a reason for your answer.
   The current has a greater effect because the amount of power dissipated (and heat produced) in a resistor is directly proportional to resistance, but it is also directly proportional to the square of the current.

Name ____________

22 Chapter Assessment

Answer the following questions, showing your calculations.

6. An electric motor operates an elevator the mass of which is 2.0×10^3 kg. The elevator rises 120 m in 32 s. The motor has a resistance while operating of 34.0 Ω and is connected across a 2.4×10^3-V source. What percentage of electric energy is converted to kinetic energy?

$E_E = mgh$
$= (2.0 \times 10^3 \text{ kg})(9.8 \text{ m/s}^2)(120 \text{ m})$
$= 2.4 \times 10^6 \text{ J}$

$I = \frac{V}{R}$
$= \frac{2.4 \times 10^3 \text{ V}}{34.0\ \Omega}$
$= 71 \text{ A}$

$E_m = I^2Rt$
$= (71 \text{ A})^2(34.0\ \Omega)(32 \text{ s})$
$= 5.5 \times 10^6 \text{ J}$

$\% = \frac{E_E}{E_m} \times 100\%$
$= \frac{2.4 \times 10^6 \text{ J}}{5.5 \times 10^6 \text{ J}} \times 100\%$
$= 44\%$

7. A three-pack of 1.5-V hearing-aid batteries costs $4.26. Each battery puts out 8.0 mA of current. Each battery lasts for 15 days. What is the cost per kilowatt hour to operate the hearing aid with one battery?

$P = VI$
$= (1.5 \text{ V})(0.0080 \text{ A})$
$= 0.012 \text{ W} = 1.2 \times 10^{-5} \text{ kW}$

$E = Pt$
$= (1.2 \times 10^{-5} \text{ kW})(360 \text{ h})$
$= 4.3 \times 10^{-3} \text{ kWh}$

$\frac{\$4.26}{3 \text{ batteries}} = \$1.42/\text{battery}$

$\frac{\$1.42}{4.3 \times 10^{-3} \text{ kWh}} = \$330/\text{kWh}$

8. While waiting for the school bus, you keep your hands warm in a pair of electric gloves. The heating element in each glove has a resistance of 8.0 Ω. Each glove operates from a 12-V source. The thermal energy produced by each glove is 640 J. You wait for the bus for 3.0 min. When the bus arrives, are the electric gloves still producing heat?

$I = \frac{V}{R} = \frac{12 \text{ V}}{8.0\ \Omega}$
$= 1.5 \text{ A}$

$t = \frac{E}{I^2R} = \frac{640 \text{ J}}{(1.5 \text{ A})^2 (8.0\ \Omega)}$
$= 36 \text{ s}$

No, they are not.

9. A model electric train makes one complete pass around a circular track every 15 s. The train's motor has a resistance of 6.0 Ω and is connected to a 70.0-V source. How much energy will the train use in 12 complete passes around the track?

$E = I^2Rt \quad I = \frac{V}{R}$

$E = \frac{V^2}{R^2}Rt = \frac{V^2t}{R} = \frac{(70.0 \text{ V})^2(180 \text{ s})}{6.0\ \Omega}$
$= 1.5 \times 10^5 \text{ J}$

Date ____________ Period ____________ Name ____________

23 Chapter Assessment

Use with Chapter 23.

Series and Parallel Circuits

Understanding Concepts Part A

Write the letter of the choice that best completes the statement or answers the question.

a 1. If four electric devices are connected in a series circuit, then the number of current paths is equal to ____.
a. one b. two c. three d. four

c 2. A series circuit contains a generator, an ammeter, and a lamp. The current in the lamp is ____.
a. equal to the current in the ammeter, but greater than the current in the generator
b. less than the current in the ammeter
c. equal to the current in the generator and equal to the current in the ammeter
d. less than the current in the generator

b 3. A series circuit contains four resistors. What is the equivalent resistance of the circuit?
a. $4R$ c. $R/4$
b. $R_1 + R_2 + R_3 + R_4$ d. $(R_1 + R_2 + R_3 + R_4)/4$

c 4. A series circuit has a 120-V generator but requires a 60-V potential source. To achieve the desired potential, a ____ can be used.
a. photoresistor c. voltage divider
b. sensor d. semiconductor

c 5. If three resistors are connected in parallel, there are ____ current paths in the circuit.
a. one b. two c. three d. four

a 6. In an electric circuit, ____ are switches that act as safety devices.
a. fuses and circuit breakers c. ammeters
b. fuses and voltage dividers d. combined circuits

For each of the statements below, write true *or* false.

7. **true** To measure the current through a resistor, an ammeter should be connected in series with the resistor.

8. **true** The equivalent resistance of a parallel circuit is always less than the resistance of any resistor in the circuit.

9. **false** A voltmeter should have a very low resistance so that it causes the largest possible changes in currents and voltages in the circuit.

10. **true** The resistance of an ammeter should be as low as possible.

11. **false** To measure the current across a resistor, connect a voltmeter in parallel with the resistor.

Name ______

23 Chapter Assessment

Understanding Concepts Part B

Answer the following questions, showing your calculations.

1. Two resistors of 3.0 Ω and 8.0 Ω are connected in series across a 9.0-V battery.
   a. What is the equivalent resistance of the circuit?
   $R = R_1 + R_2$
   $= 3.0\ \Omega + 8.0\ \Omega$
   $= 11.0\ \Omega$
   b. What is the current through the 3.0-Ω resistor?
   $I_1 = \frac{V}{R_1 + R_2} = \frac{9.0\ V}{11.0\ \Omega}$
   $= 0.82\ A$
   c. What is the current through the 8.0-Ω resistor?
   0.82 A
   d. What is the voltage drop across each resistor?
   $V_1 = IR_1$ **$V_2 = IR_2$**
   $= (0.82\ A)(3.0\ \Omega)$ **$= (0.82\ A)(8.0\ \Omega)$**
   $= 2.5\ V$ **$= 6.6\ V$**
2. A 15.0-Ω bell and an 8.0-Ω lamp are connected in parallel and placed across a difference in potential of 42 V.
   a. What is the equivalent resistance of the circuit?
   $\frac{1}{R} = \frac{1}{R_1} + \frac{1}{R_2}$
   $= \frac{1}{15.0\ \Omega} + \frac{1}{8.0\ \Omega}$
   $R = 5.2\ \Omega$
   b. What is the current in the circuit?
   $I = \frac{V}{R} = \frac{42\ V}{5.2\ V}$
   $= 8.1\ A$
   c. What is the current through each resistor?
   $I_1 = \frac{V}{R_1} = \frac{42\ V}{15.0\ \Omega}$ **$I_2 = \frac{V}{R_2} = \frac{42\ V}{8.0\ \Omega}$**
   $= 2.8\ A$ **$= 5.3\ A$**
   d. What is the voltage drop across each resistor?
   42 V across each

Name ______

23 Chapter Assessment

Applying Concepts

Answer the following questions, using complete sentences.

1. A string of holiday lights has 15 bulbs connected in series. If one of the bulbs burns out, what happens to the other bulbs? Give a reason for your answer.
   They go out because the current in the series circuit has been interrupted.
2. What happens to resistance when a resistor is added in parallel to a circuit that already has two resistors?
   As the number of parallel branches is increased, the overall resistance of the circuit decreases.
3. How is it possible to use more than one electric appliance at a time in a house?
   The electric wiring uses parallel circuits so the current in one circuit does not depend on the current in any other circuit.
4. A circuit has five identical resistors, A, B, C, D, and E. Resistors A, D, and E have the same potential difference across them. What kind of circuit is this? Give a reason for your answer.
   It is a combination series-parallel circuit. Resistors B and C are in series, and A, D, and E, which have the same potential difference across them, are in parallel.
5. What would happen to the current in a circuit if a voltmeter were substituted for an ammeter?
   An ammeter is connected in series. Its low resistance does not affect the current. If a voltmeter were substituted for the ammeter, the high resistance of the voltmeter would decrease the current.
6. Explain why a ground-fault interrupter is often required by law in electric outlets in bathrooms and kitchens, but not in other rooms in a house.
   In both of these rooms, there is plumbing. If an appliance in use touches a cold water pipe or a sink or tub full of water, it could create another current path through the user. A ground-fault interrupter detects the small difference in current this would cause and opens the circuit, preventing electric shock.
7. Why does turning on additional appliances on the same circuit breaker increase the current through the wires?
   Because the appliances are connected in parallel, each additional appliance that is turned on reduces the equivalent resistance in the circuit and causes the current to increase.

Name ____________

23 Chapter Assessment

Answer the following questions, showing your calculations.

8. Find the reading of each ammeter and each voltmeter in the diagram below.

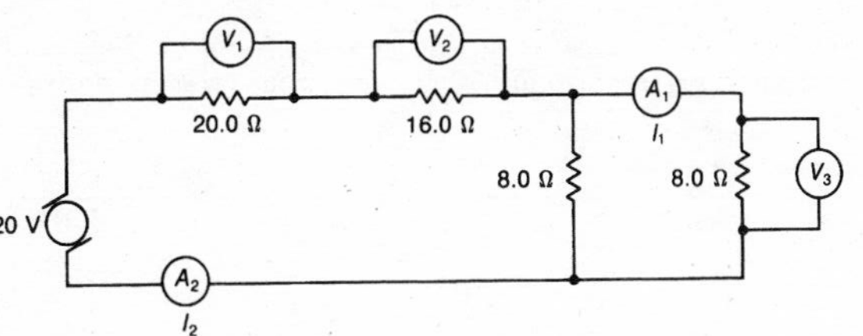

The equivalent resistance of the resistors in parallel is

$$\frac{1}{R} = \frac{1}{R_1} + \frac{1}{R_2}$$

$$= \frac{1}{8.0\ \Omega} + \frac{1}{8.0\ \Omega}$$

$$R = 4.0\ \Omega$$

For the entire circuit, the equivalent resistance is

$$R = R_1 + R_2 + R_3 = 4.0\ \Omega + 20.0\ \Omega + 16.0\ \Omega$$

$$= 40.0\ \Omega$$

$$I_{total} = I_2 = \frac{V}{R} = \frac{120\ V}{40.0\ \Omega} = 3.0\ A$$

$$V_1 = I_2 R = (3.0\ A)(20.0\ \Omega) = 60\ V$$

$$V_2 = I_2 R = (3.0\ A)(16.0\ \Omega) = 48\ V$$

The voltage drop across each 8.0-Ω resistor is

$$V_3 = IR = (3.0\ A)(4.0\ \Omega) = 12\ V$$

$$I_1 = \frac{V}{R} = \frac{12\ V}{8.0\ \Omega} = 1.5\ A$$

9. What is the power in watts used by each resistance in the diagram above?

For the 20.0-Ω resistor:
$P = I_2 V_1$
$= (3.0\ A)(60\ V)$
$= 180\ W$

For the 16-Ω resistor:
$P = I_2 V_2$
$= (3.0\ A)(48\ V)$
$= 144\ W$

For the 8-Ω resistor:
$P = I_1 V_3$
$= (1.5\ A)(12\ V)$
$= 18\ W$

Date ____________ Period ____________ Name ____________

24 Chapter Assessment

Use with Chapter 24.

Magnetic Fields

Understanding Concepts Part A

Write the letter of the choice that best completes each statement.

d 1. An object that is magnetic has _____.
- a. only a south-seeking pole
- b. only an east-seeking pole
- c. an east-seeking pole and a west-seeking pole
- d. a north-seeking pole and a south-seeking pole

a 2. The magnitude of the current in a wire is _____ to the magnetic field around the wire.
- a. proportional
- b. inversely proportional
- c. equal
- d. parallel

a 3. Increasing the number of loops in an electromagnet causes the strength of the magnetic field to _____.
- a. increase
- b. decrease
- c. remain the same
- d. double

b 4. In a magnetic material, the _____ act like tiny electromagnets.
- a. atoms
- b. electrons
- c. protons
- d. neutrons

c 5. The magnetic force on a current-carrying wire in a magnetic field is _____ the direction of the current.
- a. opposite to
- b. parallel to
- c. perpendicular to
- d. the same as

For each of the statements below, write true *or rewrite the italicized portion to make the statement true.*

6. **true** — The *magnitude* of the magnetic force on a current-carrying wire depends on the strength of the magnetic field, the current in the wire, and the length of wire in the magnetic field.

7. **repel** — When two parallel wires carry currents in opposite directions, their magnetic fields *attract* each other.

8. **a galvanometer** — A device used to measure very small electric currents is *an ammeter*.

9. **half turn** — In an electric motor, current is reversed every *complete turn*.

10. **true** — The speed of an electric motor can be controlled by *varying* the current flow.

Name ______________

24 Chapter Assessment

Understanding Concepts Part B

Answer the following questions, showing your calculations.

1. A wire carries a current of 6.0 A. The wire is at right angles to a uniform magnetic field, and 0.80 m of the wire is in the field. The force on the wire is 0.62 N. What is the strength of the magnetic field?

   $B = \frac{F}{IL}$

   $= \frac{0.62\ \text{N}}{(6.0\ \text{A})(0.80\ \text{m})}$

   $= 0.13\ \text{T}$

2. A wire is at right angles to a uniform magnetic field with magnetic induction of 0.400 T. The current through the wire is 4.00 A. What is the force that acts on the wire when 60.0 cm is in the field?

   $F = BIL$

   $= (0.400\ \text{N/A·m})(4.00\ \text{A})(0.600\ \text{m})$

   $= 0.960\ \text{N}$

3. A wire carries a current of 12 A. The wire is at right angles to a uniform magnetic field that exerts a force of 0.50 N on the wire when 2.0 m of the wire is in the field. What is the induction of the magnetic field?

   $B = \frac{F}{IL}$

   $= \frac{0.50\ \text{N}}{(12\ \text{A})(2.0\ \text{m})}$

   $= 2.1 \times 10^{-2}\ \text{T}$

4. A wire is at right angles to a magnetic field that exerts a force of 2.4 N on the wire. A current of 8.6 A flows through the wire. The induction of the magnetic field is 0.66 T. What length of wire is in the field?

   $L = \frac{F}{BI}$

   $= \frac{2.4\ \text{N}}{(0.66\ \text{N/A·m})(8.6\ \text{A})}$

   $= 0.42\ \text{m}$

5. A high-speed electron travels at right angles to a magnetic field that has an induction of 0.420 T. The electron is traveling at 3.46×10^7 m/s. What is the force acting on the electron?

   $F = Bqv$

   $= (0.420\ \text{N/A·m})(-1.60 \times 10^{-19}\ \text{C})(3.46 \times 10^7\ \text{m/s})$

   $= -2.33 \times 10^{-12}\ \text{N}$

Name ______________

24 Chapter Assessment

Applying Concepts

Answer the following questions, using complete sentences.

1. If all electrons create magnetic fields, why aren't all materials magnets?

   A magnet has electrons whose domains are aligned. If the domains of the electrons are not aligned, they cancel each other out.

2. How are the forces between charges similar to the forces between magnetic poles?

   Like charges repel and unlike charges attract. Like poles also repel and unlike poles attract.

3. Suppose you have two bar magnets. Only one of the magnets has north and south poles labeled. How would you determine which are the south and north poles on the unlabeled magnet?

   Hold the ends of the magnets near each other. The north pole of the labeled magnet will attract the south pole of the other magnet and repel the north pole.

4. An electrical wire carries current in a straight line from east to west. What is the direction of the resulting magnetic field above the wire? What is the direction of the field below the wire?

   According to the right-hand rule, the direction of the field above the wire is south to north. The direction of the field below the wire is north to south.

5. If an electromagnet is used to pick up nails and other metal objects, what happens when the current is turned off?

   Without the current there is no magnetic force; therefore, all the objects attracted by the electromagnet will be released.

6. If a permanent magnet is dropped or struck by a hammer, it may lose its magnetism. Explain why.

   Jarring the magnet may knock some domains out of alignment. If this happens, their fields will cancel each other out.

Name ______________

24 Chapter Assessment

Answer the following questions, showing your calculations.

7. A section of wire and resistors in a circuit has a total resistance of 6.0 Ω and a potential difference of 120 V. If 0.40 M of the wire is placed in a uniform magnetic field at right angles to the field, the force on the wire is 0.50 N. What is the strength of the magnetic field?

$$I = \frac{V}{R} = \frac{120\ \text{V}}{6.0\ \Omega} = 2.0 \times 10^{1}\ \text{A}$$

$$B = \frac{F}{IL} = \frac{0.50\ \text{N}}{(2.0 \times 10^{1}\ \text{A})(0.40\ \text{m})} = 0.063\ \text{T}$$

8. A proton travels at 1.0×10^{5} m/s perpendicular to a uniform magnetic field of 5.5×10^{-5} T. What is the magnitude of the acceleration of the proton?

$$F = Bqv = ma$$

$$a = \frac{Bqv}{m} = \frac{(5.5 \times 10^{-5}\ \text{T})(1.60 \times 10^{-19}\ \text{C})(1.0 \times 10^{5}\ \text{m/s})}{1.673 \times 10^{-27}\ \text{kg}} = 5.3 \times 10^{8}\ \text{m/s}^2$$

Date ______________ Period ______________ Name ______________

25 Chapter Assessment

Use with Chapter 25.

Electromagnetic Induction

Understanding Concepts Part A

For each of the statements below, write true *or rewrite the italicized part to make the statement true.*

1. An electric current is generated in a wire when the wire is moved so that it *cuts across* magnetic field lines.
true

2. Current can be made to flow in a stationary wire by moving a magnetic field *parallel* to the wire.
across

3. The electromotive force depends only on magnetic field strength, the length of the wire in the magnetic field, and the *velocity* of the wire in the magnetic field.
true

4. An electric generator converts mechanical energy to *thermal* energy.
electric

5. An electric motor is almost identical in construction to an electric generator, but the motor converts electric energy to *mechanical* energy.
true

6. According to Lenz's law, the direction of induced current is such that the magnetic field resulting from the induced current *strengthens* the change in field that caused the current.
opposes

7. If a generator produces only a small current, then the opposing force on the armature will be small and the armature will be *hard* to turn.
easy

8. When a motor is first turned on, a *large* current flows because of the low resistance of the motor.
true

9. If the N-pole of a magnet is moved toward the right end of a coil of wire, the right end of the coil becomes an N-pole and *attracts* the magnet.
repels

10. When a piece of metal is moved through a magnetic field, *eddy currents* are generated in the metal.
true

11. In a *step-up* transformer, the primary voltage is greater than the secondary voltage.
step-down

Name ______________

25 Chapter Assessment

Understanding Concepts Part B

Answer the following questions, showing your calculations.

1. A wire 42.0 m long moves directly upward through a magnetic field of 6.20×10^{-4} T at a speed of 18.0 m/s. What *EMF* is induced in the wire?

   $EMF = BLv$

   $= (6.20 \times 10^{-4}\ \text{T})(42.0\ \text{m})(18.0\ \text{m/s})$

   $= 0.469\ \text{V}$

2. An AC generator develops a maximum *EMF* of 620 V. What effective *EMF* does the generator deliver to an external circuit?

   $V_{eff} = 0.707\ V_{max}$

   $= 0.707(620\ \text{V})$

   $= 438\ \text{V}$

3. A step-up transformer has 125 turns on its primary coil. Its secondary coil consists of 1440 turns. The primary coil receives an AC current at 120 V.

   a. What is the voltage across the secondary circuit?

   $\frac{V_s}{V_p} = \frac{N_s}{N_p}$ $\quad V_s = \frac{V_p N_s}{N_p}$

   $= \frac{(120\ \text{V})(1440)}{125}$

   $= 1.38 \times 10^3\ \text{V}$

   b. The current in the secondary coil is 3.6 A. What current flows in the primary circuit?

   $V_p I_p = V_s I_s$ $\quad I_p = \frac{V_s I_s}{V_p}$

   $= \frac{(1380\ \text{V})(3.6\ \text{A})}{120\ \text{V}}$

   $= 41\ \text{A}$

   c. What is the power input and output of the transformer?

   $P_p = V_p I_p$ $\quad P_s = V_s I_s$

   $= (120\ \text{V})(41\ \text{A})$ $\quad = (1.4 \times 10^3\ \text{V})(3.6\ \text{A})$

   $= 4.9 \times 10^3\ \text{W}$ $\quad = 5.0 \times 10^3\ \text{W}$

4. The primary coil of a transformer has 640 turns and is connected to a 240-V source. How many turns would be needed in the secondary coil to supply 800 V?

   $\frac{V_s}{V_p} = \frac{N_s}{N_p}$ $\quad N_s = \frac{N_p V_s}{V_p}$

   $= \frac{(640)(800\ \text{V})}{240\ \text{V}}$

   $= 2.1 \times 10^3$

Name ______________

25 Chapter Assessment

Applying Concepts

Answer the following questions, using complete sentences.

1. A loop of wire is connected to a galvanometer. If a bar magnet is dropped through the loop, what happens to the galvanometer?

   The galvanometer registers a current produced in the loop of wire as the magnetic field of the magnet crosses the conducting wire.

2. A bar magnet and a loop of wire are moving parallel to each other at the same velocity. What is the voltage induced in the loop? Give a reason for your answer.

   The voltage is zero. No current is induced because the conductor is not moving through the magnetic field.

3. What happens to induced *EMF* when magnetic field strength is doubled?

   Since *EMF* is directly proportional to magnetic field strength, it doubles.

4. Compare the operation of an electric motor with that of an electric generator.

   In an electric motor, a voltage is placed across an armature coil in a magnetic field. The voltage causes current to flow in the coil, and the armature turns. In a generator, mechanical energy turns an armature in a magnetic field.

5. Why do the lights in a room dim momentarily when a large appliance is turned on?

   The heavy current required to start a motor causes a voltage drop across the wires that carry current to the motor. In turn, the voltage across the motor drops, along with the voltage of lights connected in parallel near the motor.

6. What happens to the primary voltage when the number of turns on a secondary transformer coil is doubled?

   Since primary voltage is inversely proportional to the number of turns on the secondary coil, doubling the turns cuts the primary voltage in half.

Name ______________

25 Chapter Assessment

Answer the following questions, showing your calculations.

7. The current flowing through a wire is 2.4×10^{-3} A. The wire is connected across a circuit of 8.0-Ω resistance. If 0.60 m of the wire is moving perpendicularly through the magnetic field of 0.48 T, what is the velocity of the wire?

$IR = BLv$ $\quad v = \frac{IR}{BL}$

$= \frac{(2.4 \times 10^{-3}\ \text{A})(8.0\ \Omega)}{(0.48\ \text{T})(0.60\ \text{m})}$

$= 6.7 \times 10^{-2}$ m/s

8. A space vehicle is sent to Jupiter to explore the planet's properties from orbit. The vehicle travels 1.0×10^3 km/min. When in orbit, the probe deploys a horizontal antenna that is 120 m long. Data received on Earth indicate that the probe is flying over a location where the magnetic field is 0.18 T. What voltage is induced between the antenna's tips?

$EMF = BLv$ $\quad v = \frac{d}{t}$

$EMF = \frac{BLd}{t}$

$= \frac{(0.18\ \text{T})(120\ \text{m})(1.0 \times 10^6\ \text{m})}{60\ \text{s}}$

$= 3.6 \times 10^5$ V

9. An alternating-current generator requires 120 J of mechanical energy per second to produce 100 W of effective power.

a. What is the efficiency of the generator?

$\text{efficiency} = \frac{\text{power out}}{\text{power in}} \times 100\%$

$= \frac{100\ \text{W}}{120\ \text{W}} \times 100\%$

$= 83\%$

b. If the total resistance of turns in the wire in the generator is 12 Ω, what is the maximum current produced?

$P_{AC} = I_{eff}^2 R$

$I_{eff} = \sqrt{\frac{P_{AC}}{R}}$

$= \sqrt{\frac{100\ \text{W}}{12\ \Omega}}$

$= 2.9$ A

$I_{max} = \frac{I_{eff}}{0.707}$

$= \frac{2.9\ \text{A}}{0.707}$

$= 4.1$ A

Date ______ Period ______ Name ______________

26 Chapter Assessment

Use with Chapter 26.

Electromagnetism

Understanding Concepts Part A

Write the letter of the choice that best completes each statement.

a **1.** In a cathode-ray tube, an electric field pulls electrons out of the ____ toward the ____.
- **a.** negatively charged cathode, positively charged anode
- **b.** positively charged anode, negatively charged cathode
- **c.** negatively charged anode, positively charged cathode
- **d.** positively charged cathode, negatively charged anode

d **2.** The masses of positive ions can be measured precisely using a ____.
- **a.** Thomson tube
- **b.** Bainbridge tube
- **c.** cathode-ray tube
- **d.** mass spectrometer

a **3.** In an electromagnetic wave, the electric and magnetic fields are ____ to each other and ____ to the direction of wave motion.
- **a.** at right angles, perpendicular
- **b.** at right angles, parallel
- **c.** parallel, at right angles
- **d.** opposite, parallel

b **4.** To produce an electromagnetic wave, an antenna can be connected to ____.
- **a.** a battery
- **b.** an alternating current source
- **c.** a direct current source
- **d.** a magnet

c **5.** An electromagnetic wave produced by an antenna is ____.
- **a.** perpendicular to the direction of the antenna wires
- **b.** independent of the direction of the antenna wires
- **c.** parallel to the direction of the antenna wires
- **d.** dependent on the direction of the current

For each of the statements below, write true *or* false.

6. **false** An electromagnetic wave can be produced only by an antenna connected to an alternating current source.

7. **true** Quartz crystals have a property called piezoelectricity that can generate electromagnetic waves.

8. **true** The *EMF* across the terminals of a reception antenna is largest if the length of the antenna is one-half the wavelength of the wave.

9. **true** Waves carry energy as well as information.

10. **false** X rays are in the same range of wavelengths as visible light.

Name ______________

26 Chapter Assessment

Understanding Concepts Part B

Answer the following questions, showing your calculations.

1. An object passes through a magnetic field of 6.2×10^{-2} T. The object's speed is 8.4×10^{3} m/s. What is the electric field intensity?

   $E = Bv$

   $= (6.2 \times 10^{-2}\ \text{T})(8.4 \times 10^{3}\ \text{m/s})$

   $= 5.2 \times 10^{2}\ \text{N/C}$

2. An unknown particle having a mass of 2.4×20^{-27} kg and a charge of 3.2×10^{-19} C passes through a magnetic field of 5.6×10^{-1} T. The velocity of the particle is 6.8×10^{3} m/s. What is the radius of its path?

   $r = \frac{mv}{Bq}$

   $= \frac{(2.4 \times 10^{-27}\ \text{kg})(6.8 \times 10^{3}\ \text{m/s})}{(5.6 \times 10^{-1}\ \text{T})(3.2 \times 10^{-19}\ \text{C})}$

   $= 9.1 \times 10^{-5}\ \text{m}$

3. A particle with a mass of 4.1×10^{-27} kg and a charge of 6.4×10^{-19} C crosses a magnetic field that measures 2.6×10^{-2} T. The particle assumes a circular path with a radius of 1.2×10^{-1} m. At what speed is the particle moving?

   $v = \frac{Brq}{m}$

   $= \frac{(2.6 \times 10^{-2}\ \text{T})(1.2 \times 10^{-1}\ \text{m})(6.4 \times 10^{-19}\ \text{C})}{4.1 \times 10^{-27}\ \text{kg}}$

   $= 4.9 \times 10^{5}\ \text{m/s}$

4. A particle passing through a magnetic field has a mass of 6.5×10^{-27} kg and is moving at 3.2×10^{4} m/s. The charge on the particle is 2.5×10^{-18} C and the radius of its circular path through the field is 4.1×10^{-2} m. What is the strength of the magnetic field?

   $B = \frac{mv}{qr}$

   $= \frac{(6.5 \times 10^{-27}\ \text{kg})(3.2 \times 10^{4}\ \text{m/s})}{(2.5 \times 10^{-18}\ \text{C})(4.1 \times 10^{-2}\ \text{m})}$

   $= 2.0 \times 10^{-3}\ \text{T}$

5. A particle with a mass of 3.34×10^{-27} kg and a charge of 1.6×10^{-19} C passes through a magnetic field of 3.8×10^{-3} T. This causes the nucleus to assume a circular path with a radius of 0.060 m. A potential difference of what value accelerated the particle?

   $\Delta V = \frac{qB^2r^2}{2m}$

   $= \frac{(1.6 \times 10^{-19}\ \text{C})(3.8 \times 10^{-3}\ \text{T})^2 (6.0 \times 10^{-2}\ \text{m})^2}{2(3.34 \times 10^{-27}\ \text{kg})}$

   $= 1.2\ \text{V}$

Name ______________

26 Chapter Assessment

Applying Concepts

1. A scientist wants to know how much of a given pollutant is found in the air near a factory. Ordinarily, the pollutant is found in minute amounts. How might the scientist obtain this information?

   Tiny amounts of a substance can be detected with a mass spectrometer. The ions that make up the pollutant can be separated and identified on the basis of their masses.

2. What is piezoelectricity? How does it produce an electromagnetic field?

   Piezoelectricity is the ability of a substance to bend when a voltage is applied across it. When a quartz crystal vibrates, it generates an *EMF* at the same frequency as its vibration. The changing *EMF* generates an electromagnetic wave.

3. Explain what happens when you change the setting on your radio from one station to another.

   The capacitance of the circuit adjusts so that the oscillation frequency of the circuit is equal to the frequency of the wave emitted by the desired radio station.

4. If the orientation of the electric and magnetic fields generated by an electromagnetic wave is known, is it possible to determine the direction of the motion of the wave? Give a reason for your answer.

   Yes. The electric and magnetic fields are perpendicular to each other and to the direction of wave propagation.

5. Briefly explain how an electromagnetic wave is produced by the antenna of a television broadcast station.

   The antenna is connected to an alternating current source. The changing current in the antenna creates a changing electric field, which moves outward from the antenna. The changing electric field generates a changing magnetic field that also moves outward. The electric field and magnetic field together make up an electromagnetic wave.

6. Why did Thomson use the charge-to-mass ratio to find the mass of an electron?

   The mass of an electron is too small to be measured directly. Since the charge on an electron was already known, however, the mass of the electron could be calculated from the charge-to-mass ratio.

Name ______________

26 Chapter Assessment

Answer the following questions, showing your calculations.

7. In an attempt to identify an unknown atom, a research team has narrowed the possibilities to a few atoms. The nuclear composition (protons and neutrons) of several atoms is shown in the table below. Each proton or neutron has a mass of 1.67×10^{-24} kg. Experiments have yielded the following data: The ion of the atom has a negative charge of 1.6×10^{-19} C. When passing through a magnetic field of 7.8×10^{-3} T at a speed of 7.9 m/s, the ion develops a circular path that has a radius of 8.3×10^{-4} m. What is the identity of the atom?

Atom	Protons	Neutrons
chlorine	17	18
argon	18	22
bromine	35	44
krypton	36	48
iodine	53	74

$$m = \frac{Bqr}{v} = \frac{(7.8 \times 10^{-3}\ \text{T})(1.6 \times 10^{-19}\ \text{C})(8.3 \times 10^{-4}\ \text{m})}{7.9\ \text{m/s}} = 1.3 \times 10^{-25}\ \text{kg}$$

Because the mass of the electron removed to make the ion is so small, it can be assumed that ion mass = atom mass.

$$\text{number of protons and neutrons} = \frac{\text{mass of atom}}{\text{mass of proton or neutron}} = \frac{1.3 \times 10^{-25}\ \text{kg}}{1.67 \times 10^{-27}\ \text{kg}} \approx 78$$

The atom whose combined number of protons and neutrons is closest to 78 is bromine, which has a total of 79 protons and neutrons.

8. Radon, Rn, is a radioactive element. As such it releases certain particles. Assume you are a researcher attempting to identify the particle released. It has a charge of 3.2×10^{-19} C. When passing through a magnetic field of 2.0 T across a potential difference of 1.6×10^{7} V, the particle follows a circular path that has a radius of 4.1×10^{-1} m. What is the mass of the particle?

$$m = \frac{qB^2r^2}{2V} = \frac{(3.2 \times 10^{-19}\ \text{C})(2.0\ \text{T})^2(4.1 \times 10^{-1}\ \text{m})^2}{2(1.6 \times 10^{7}\ \text{V})} = 6.7 \times 10^{-27}\ \text{kg}$$

Date ________ Period ________ Name ______________

27 Chapter Assessment

Use with Chapter 27.

Quantum Theory

Understanding Concepts Part A

Write the letter of the choice that best completes each statement.

a 1. According to Planck's hypothesis, ____.
- a. the energy of an incandescent body is quantized
- b. the variable n can have any real number value
- c. the frequency of vibration is inversely proportional to the energy
- d. atoms constantly radiate electromagnetic waves when they vibrate

c 2. If the incident light on a photocell is very dim, electrons will ____.
- a. never be ejected
- b. be ejected only after they have absorbed energy for a long time
- c. be ejected immediately if the frequency is at or above the threshold frequency
- d. be ejected after a long time if the frequency is below the threshold frequency

a 3. The slope of a graph of the kinetic energy of ejected electrons versus the frequency of the incident radiation is equal to ____.
- a. Planck's constant
- b. the wavelength of the radiation
- c. the work function
- d. the threshold frequency

c 4. Compton's X-ray experiment showed that ____.
- a. only photons behave like particles
- b. only electrons behave like particles
- c. momentum and kinetic energy are conserved when photons collide with electrons
- d. photons have more mass than electrons

For each of the statements below, write true *or rewrite the italicized part to make the statement true.*

5. **increases** In a star's spectrum, the frequency of the radiation emitted increases as the star's temperature *decreases*.

6. **true** Einstein theorized that the momentum of a photon is *inversely* proportional to the wavelength.

7. **true** The wavelength of a particle is *inversely proportional* to the particle's momentum.

8. **momentum** Because of the Compton effect, when light of short wavelengths is used to measure the location of a particle, the particle's *position* is changed.

9. **true** The *Heisenberg uncertainty principle* says that it is impossible to measure precisely both the position and momentum of a particle at the same time.

Name ____________

27 Chapter Assessment

Understanding Concepts Part B

Answer the following questions, showing your calculations.

1. The stopping potential of a photocell is 2.5 V. What kinetic energy does the incident light give to the electrons? Give your answer in joules and electron volts.

$K = -qV_0$

$= -(-1.60 \times 10^{-19}\ \text{C})(2.5\ \text{J/C})$

$= 4.0 \times 10^{-19}\ \text{J} = (4.0 \times 10^{-19}\ \text{J})\left(\frac{1\ \text{eV}}{1.6 \times 10^{-19}\ \text{J}}\right)$

$= 2.5\ \text{eV}$

2. A certain photoelectric surface has a threshold frequency of 4.62×10^{14} Hz.

a. What is the photoelectric work function in joules?

$W = hf_0$

$= (6.63 \times 10^{-34}\ \text{J/Hz})(4.62 \times 10^{14}\ \text{Hz})$

$= 3.06 \times 10^{-19}\ \text{J}$

b. The surface is illuminated with light that has a frequency of 5.2×10^{14} Hz. What is the kinetic energy of the electrons ejected from the surface? Give your answer in joules and electron volts.

$K = hf - hf_0$

$= (6.63 \times 10^{-34}\ \text{J/Hz})(5.2 \times 10^{14}\ \text{Hz}) - (6.63 \times 10^{-34}\ \text{J/Hz})(4.6 \times 10^{14}\ \text{Hz})$

$= 4.0 \times 10^{-20}\ \text{J}$

$= (4.0 \times 10^{-20}\ \text{J})\left(\frac{1\ \text{eV}}{1.6 \times 10^{-19}\ \text{J}}\right)$

$= 0.25\ \text{eV}$

3. An X ray traveling in a vacuum has a wavelength of 4.2×10^{-12} m. What is the momentum of the wave?

$p = \frac{h}{\lambda}$

$= \frac{6.63 \times 10^{-34}\ \text{J·s}}{4.2 \times 10^{-12}\ \text{m}}$

$= 1.6 \times 10^{-22}\ \text{kg·m/s}$

4. What is the de Broglie wavelength of a 1.00-kg object traveling at 45.0 m/s?

$\lambda = \frac{h}{mv}$

$= \frac{6.63 \times 10^{-34}\ \text{J·s}}{(1.00\ \text{kg})(45.0\ \text{m/s})}$

$= 1.47 \times 10^{-35}\ \text{m}$

Name ____________

27 Chapter Assessment

Applying Concepts

Answer the following questions, using complete sentences.

1. What conditions must exist to produce a current in a photocell? Does all radiation result in a current? Give a reason for your answer.

To produce a current, radiation must hit the cathode. Not all radiation results in a current because electrons are ejected only if the frequency of radiation is at or above the threshold frequency.

2. Compare the predictions of the electromagnetic wave theory and the photon theory when radiation shines on a metal plate. Which one more accurately describes the photoelectric effect?

The electromagnetic theory states that the more intense the radiation, regardless of the frequency, the stronger the electric and magnetic fields. Therefore, radiation with a low intensity would require that the electrons absorb energy for a long time to acquire enough energy to be ejected. The photon theory, on the other hand, explains the photoelectric effect by proposing that light and other forms of radiation consist of discrete bundles of energy called photons. The energy of each photon depends on the frequency of light. Therefore, when the frequency of the radiation is above the threshold frequency, electrons are ejected immediately. The photon theory more accurately describes the photoelectric effect.

3. What happens to the energy of a photon as it interacts with an electron of a metal?

Part of the photon's energy frees the electron from the metal. The remaining energy becomes the kinetic energy of the electron.

4. What do both the Compton effect and the photoelectric effect indicate about electromagnetic radiation?

Electromagnetic radiation has particle-like properties.

5. In the 1920s, a scientist suggested that material particles have wave properties. What evidence was discovered that supports this suggestion?

When a beam of electrons is aimed at a very thin crystal, the crystal acts like a diffraction grating. The electrons are diffracted by the crystal and form the same pattern as are formed by X rays of a similar wavelength.

6. Explain the Heisenberg uncertainty principle.

The principle states that measuring either a particle's momentum or its position changes the other variable. As a result, both variables—position and momentum—cannot be known precisely at the same instant in time.

Name ____________

27 Chapter Assessment

Answer the following questions, showing your calculations.

7. The emission of X rays can be described as an inverse photoelectric effect. What is the potential difference through which an electron accelerates to produce an X ray with a wavelength of 0.10 nm?

$$f = \frac{c}{\lambda} = \frac{3.0 \times 10^{8}\ \text{m/s}}{1.0 \times 10^{-10}\ \text{m}} = 3.0 \times 10^{18}\ \text{s}^{-1}$$

$$V_0 = \frac{K}{-q} = \frac{hf}{-q} = \frac{(6.63 \times 10^{-34}\ \text{J·s})(3.0 \times 10^{18}\ \text{s}^{-1})}{-(-1.60 \times 10^{-19}\ \text{C})} = 1.2 \times 10^{4}\ \text{V}$$

8. A potential difference of 200 V accelerates an electron. What is the de Broglie wavelength of the electron? (The mass of an electron is 9.11×10^{-31} kg.)

$$K = \frac{1}{2}mv^2 \qquad K = -qV_0$$

$$v = \sqrt{\frac{2K}{m}} \qquad v = \sqrt{\frac{2(-qV_0)}{m}} = \sqrt{\frac{-2(-1.6 \times 10^{-19}\ \text{C})(200\ \text{V})}{9.11 \times 10^{-31}\ \text{kg}}} = 8.4 \times 10^{6}\ \text{m/s}$$

$$\lambda = \frac{h}{mv} = \frac{6.63 \times 10^{-34}\ \text{J·s}}{(9.11 \times 10^{-31}\ \text{kg})(8.4 \times 10^{6}\ \text{m/s})} = 8.7 \times 10^{-11}\ \text{m}$$

9. The threshold frequency of sodium is 5.6×10^{14} Hz. If light of frequency 7.8×10^{14} Hz illuminates sodium, electrons are emitted. How fast does one of these electrons travel?

$$K = \frac{1}{2}mv^2 = hf - hf_0$$

$$v = \sqrt{\frac{2h(f - f_0)}{m}} = \sqrt{\frac{2(6.63 \times 10^{-34}\ \text{J/Hz})(7.8 \times 10^{14}\ \text{Hz} - 5.6 \times 10^{14}\ \text{Hz})}{9.11 \times 10^{-31}\ \text{kg}}} = 5.7 \times 10^{5}\ \text{m/s}$$

Date ____________ Period ____________ Name ____________

28 Chapter Assessment

Use with Chapter 28.

The Atom

Understanding Concepts Part A

Write the letter of the choice that best completes the statement or answers the question.

__b__ **1.** The results of Rutherford's gold-foil experiment indicated that ____.
- **a.** positive charge is spread throughout the atom
- **b.** positive charge is concentrated in a tiny nucleus
- **c.** electrons exist in the nucleus
- **d.** the nucleus has no electric charge

__b__ **2.** Which of the following is characteristic of the emission spectrum for a gas?
- **a.** a continuous band of colors from red through violet
- **b.** a series of separate lines of different colors
- **c.** a band of colors with occasional dark lines
- **d.** bands of color alternating with bands of darkness

__a__ **3.** An electron in the ground state ____.
- **a.** is at the lowest energy level
- **b.** can emit energy
- **c.** can remain in that state for only a fraction of a second
- **d.** can move to a lower energy level

__d__ **4.** The Bohr model of the atom cannot be used to ____.
- **a.** determine the energy levels of hydrogen
- **b.** account for the chemical properties of hydrogen
- **c.** calculate the ionization energy of hydrogen
- **d.** account for the wave properties of the electron in hydrogen

__c__ **5.** The region with a high probability of having an electron is ____.
- **a.** the Bohr orbit
- **b.** the nucleus
- **c.** the electron cloud
- **d.** the absorption band

For each of the statements below, write true *or rewrite the italicized part to make the statement true.*

6. __true__ The symbol *n* stands for the principal quantum number.

7. __coherent__ The light emitted by lasers is *incoherent*.

8. __$nh/2\pi$__ Angular momentum is equal to $2\pi r$.

9. __true__ When an electron moves from the ground state to an excited state, it *absorbs* energy.

Name ______________

28 Chapter Assessment

Understanding Concepts Part B

Answer the following questions, showing your calculations.

1. Calculate the radius of the orbit of a hydrogen electron at the $n = 4$ level, given that the radius for the $n = 1$ level is 0.053 nm.

   $r_n = (0.053\text{ nm})n^2$

   $r_4 = (0.053\text{ nm})4^2$

   $= 0.85\text{ nm}$

2. What is the energy of a photon emitted when a hydrogen electron drops from the $n = 3$ level to the $n = 2$ level?

   $E_n = \frac{-13.6\text{ eV}}{n^2}$

   $E_i = \frac{-13.6\text{ eV}}{3^2}$

   $= -1.51\text{ eV}$

   $E_f = \frac{-13.6\text{ eV}}{2^2}$

   $= -3.40\text{ eV}$

   $\Delta E = E_i - E_f$

   $= -1.51\text{ eV} - (-3.40\text{ eV})$

   $= 1.89\text{ eV}$

3. What are the frequency and wavelength of the photon in problem 2?

   $f = \frac{(\Delta E)(1.61 \times 10^{-19}\text{ J/eV})}{h}$

   $= \frac{(1.89\text{ eV})(1.61 \times 10^{-19}\text{ J/eV})}{6.63 \times 10^{-34}\text{ J/Hz}}$

   $= 4.59 \times 10^{14}\text{ Hz}$

   $\lambda = \frac{c}{f}$

   $= \frac{3.00 \times 10^{8}\text{ m/s}}{4.59 \times 10^{14}\text{ Hz}}$

   $= 6.54 \times 10^{-7}\text{ m}$

4. Heated mercury vapor produces a spectral line with a wavelength of 245 nm. Calculate the energy, in electron volts, of the photon emitted.

   $E = \frac{hc}{\lambda}$

   $= \frac{(6.63 \times 10^{-34}\text{ J/Hz})(3.00 \times 10^{8}\text{ m/s})}{(2.45 \times 10^{-7}\text{ m})(1.61 \times 10^{-19}\text{ J/eV})}$

   $= 5.07\text{ eV}$

5. Calculate the energy of the photons emitted by each of the following three transitions of a hydrogen electron: $n = 5$ to $n = 3$; $n = 6$ to $n = 2$; and $n = 2$ to $n = 1$. Which transition releases the most energetic photon?

   $E_n = \frac{-13.6\text{ eV}}{n^2}$

   $E_5 = -0.544\text{ eV}$, $E_3 = -1.51\text{ eV}$; $\Delta E = 0.97\text{ eV}$

   $E_6 = -0.378\text{ eV}$, $E_2 = -3.40\text{ eV}$; $\Delta E = 3.02\text{ eV}$

   $E_2 = -3.40\text{ eV}$, $E_1 = -13.6\text{ eV}$; $\Delta E = 10.2\text{ eV}$

   The transition $n = 2$ to $n = 1$ produces the most energetic photon.

Name ______________

28 Chapter Assessment

Applying Concepts

Answer the following questions, using complete sentences.

1. Explain why line spectra can be thought of as "atomic fingerprints."

   The spectrum of each kind of atom is unique and thus can be used to identify the atom, just as fingerprints are unique to each person and can be used to identify a person.

2. Distinguish between the ground state and an excited state of an electron.

   In the ground state, an electron has the lowest amount of energy possible. An electron in that state can gain energy and move to a higher energy level, known as an excited state. The electron can stay in an excited state for a very short time.

3. Explain why electrons in an atom do not fall into the nucleus.

   Electrons would fall into the nucleus only if they radiated electromagnetic energy. However, electrons have wave characteristics, can exist indefinitely in the electron cloud without radiating energy, and thus do not collapse into the nucleus.

4. How does the quantum model of the atom differ from the Bohr model?

   According to the quantum model, electrons have wave properties as well as particle properties, and these account for the quantization of energy. They are in the electron cloud, and only probability information can be gathered on their location and movement. According to the Bohr model, electrons are particles that orbit at fixed distances.

5. Explain line spectra in terms of the quantum model of the atom.

   Because energy in an atom is quantized, energy emissions have discrete values—that is, the photons emitted during transitions have particular frequencies and wavelengths. These discrete values are represented by the lines in line spectra.

6. Why is the word *avalanche* often used to describe the operation of a laser?

   Producing the photons in laser light involves stimulated emission. The emission begins with individual atoms but rapidly affects more and more atoms, causing more and more photons to be released, creating an avalanchelike effect.

Name ______________________

28 Chapter Assessment

Answer the following questions, showing your calculations.

7. A laser emits light that has a wavelength of 633 nm.

a. What is the energy, in joules, of a photon emitted by the laser?

$$E = \frac{hc}{\lambda}$$

$$= \frac{(6.63 \times 10^{-34}\ \text{J/Hz})(3.00 \times 10^{8}\ \text{m/s})}{(6.33 \times 10^{-7}\ \text{m})}$$

$$= 3.14 \times 10^{-19}\ \text{J}$$

b. The power of the laser is 0.5 W, and the laser pulses are 20 ms long. How much total energy does a single pulse have? (Recall that power = energy/time, and that 1 W = 1 J/s.)

$$E = \text{power} \times \text{time}$$

$$= (0.5\ \text{W})(20 \times 10^{-3}\ \text{s})\left(\frac{1\ \text{J/s}}{1\ \text{W}}\right)$$

$$= 0.01\ \text{J}$$

c. How many photons are in one pulse of the laser?

$$\text{number of photons} = \frac{\text{total energy of pulse}}{\text{energy per photon}}$$

$$= \frac{0.01\ \text{J}}{3.14 \times 10^{-19}\ \text{J}}$$

$$= 3 \times 10^{16}$$

8. Assume that the Bohr model of the atom is correct. Calculate the velocity of an electron in the first Bohr orbit, given that the mass of an electron is 9.11×10^{-31} kg.

$$r_n = (0.053\ \text{nm})n^2$$

$$r_1 = (0.053\ \text{nm})1^2$$

$$= 0.053\ \text{nm}$$

$$mvr = \frac{nh}{2\pi}$$

$$v = \frac{nh}{mr2\pi}$$

$$= \frac{(1)(6.63 \times 10^{-34}\ \text{J/Hz})}{(9.11 \times 10^{-31}\ \text{kg})(0.053 \times 10^{-9}\ \text{m})(2\pi)}$$

$$= 2.19 \times 10^{6}\ \text{m/s}$$

9. Derive a formula to determine an electron's velocity, given its angular momentum and wavelength.

$$mvr = \frac{hr}{\lambda}$$

$$v = \frac{hr}{\lambda mr}$$

$$v = \frac{h}{\lambda m}$$

Date __________ Period __________ Name ______________________

29 Chapter Assessment

Use with Chapter 29.

Solid State Electronics

Understanding Concepts Part A

Write the letter of the choice that best completes each statement.

__b__ **1.** When a potential difference is put across a wire, _____.
- **a.** electron speeds decrease
- **b.** electrons drift slowly toward the positive end of the wire
- **c.** conduction of electricity ceases
- **d.** electron energies lessen

__a__ **2.** In a conductor, conductivity increases as _____.
- **a.** temperature decreases
- **b.** temperature increases
- **c.** resistance increases
- **d.** more electrons move into the valence band

__d__ **3.** Compared to the forbidden gap in an insulator, the forbidden gap in a semiconductor is _____.
- **a.** much larger
- **b.** slightly larger
- **c.** the same size
- **d.** smaller

__c__ **4.** Impurity atoms that increase conductivity are added to a pure semiconductor to produce _____.
- **a.** a conductor
- **b.** an insulator
- **c.** an extrinsic semiconductor
- **d.** an intrinsic semiconductor

__a__ **5.** When dopants are added to a semiconductor, the net charge of the material _____.
- **a.** remains zero
- **b.** becomes zero
- **c.** becomes positive
- **d.** becomes negative

__b__ **6.** A diode whose holes and free electrons are drawn toward the battery has been _____.
- **a.** forward-biased
- **b.** reverse-biased
- **c.** converted to a transistor
- **d.** given a net charge

__c__ **7.** Dopants increase conductivity by _____.
- **a.** creating an electric field
- **b.** decreasing the temperature
- **c.** providing electrons or holes
- **d.** increasing resistance

Name ______________

29 Chapter Assessment

For each of the statements below, write true *or* false.

true 8. When two atoms are brought together in a solid, the electric field of one atom affects the field of the other atom.

false 9. A rectifier is a diode used to convert voltage that has only one polarity to AC voltage.

true 10. The highest band that contains electrons is called the valence band.

true 11. When a hole and a free electron combine, their charges cancel each other.

false 12. Miniaturization of integrated circuits does not affect the speed of computers.

Understanding Concepts Part B

Answer the following questions, showing your calculations.

1. Zinc has a density of 7.13 g/cm^3. Its atomic mass is 65.37 g/mol. If zinc has two free electrons per atom, how many free electrons are in a cubic centimeter of zinc?

$$\frac{\text{free e}^-}{\text{cm}^3} = \left(\frac{2 \text{ free e}^-}{\text{atom}}\right)\left(\frac{6.02 \times 10^{23} \text{ atoms}}{\text{mol}}\right)\left(\frac{1 \text{ mol}}{65.37\text{g}}\right)\left(\frac{7.13 \text{ g}}{\text{cm}^3}\right)$$

$$= 1.31 \times 10^{23} \text{ free e}^-/\text{cm}^3$$

2. Calculate the density of copper, given that each copper atom contributes one free electron and there are 8.49×10^{22} free e$^-$/cm^3 Cu. The atomic mass of copper is 63.54 g/mol.

$$\text{density} = \left(\frac{1 \text{ atom}}{\text{free e}^-}\right)\left(\frac{8.49 \times 10^{22} \text{ free e}^-}{\text{cm}^3}\right)\left(\frac{1 \text{ mol}}{6.02 \times 10^{23} \text{ atoms}}\right)\left(\frac{63.54 \text{ g}}{\text{mol}}\right)$$

$$= 8.96 \text{ g/cm}^3$$

3. Find the number of free electrons per cubic centimeter in silicon at room temperature, given that there are 2×10^{-10} free electrons per atom. The density and molar mass of silicon are 2.33 g/cm^3 and 28.09 g/mol.

$$\frac{\text{free e}^-}{\text{cm}^3} = \left(\frac{2 \times 10^{-10} \text{ free e}^-}{\text{atom}}\right)\left(\frac{6.02 \times 10^{23} \text{ atoms}}{\text{mol}}\right)\left(\frac{1 \text{ mol}}{28.09\text{g}}\right)\left(\frac{2.33 \text{ g}}{\text{cm}^3}\right)$$

$$= 1 \times 10^{13} \text{ free e}^-/\text{cm}^3$$

4. In a forward-biased silicon diode, the current is 22 mA and the voltage is 0.7 V. If the diode is connected to a battery through a 450-Ω resistor, what is the voltage of the battery?

$$V_b = IR + V_d$$
$$= (0.022 \text{ A})(450 \ \Omega) + 0.7 \ V$$
$$= 11 \ V$$

5. A forward-biased silicon diode is connected to a 12.0-V battery through a resistor. If the current is 12 mA and the voltage is 0.7 V, what is the resistance?

$$V_b = IR + V_d$$
$$R = \frac{V_b - V_d}{I}$$
$$= \frac{12.0 \text{ V} - 0.7 \text{ V}}{0.012 \text{ A}}$$
$$= 9.40 \times 10^2 \ \Omega$$

Name ______________

29 Chapter Assessment

Applying Concepts

Answer the following questions, using complete sentences.

1. Contrast the energy bands of conductors and of insulators.
In conductors, the bands are partially filled, and there is essentially no forbidden gap. There are more spaces in the lowest band than there are electrons to fill them. In insulators, the valence band is filled, the conduction band is empty, and there is a wide forbidden gap between them.

2. Why is silicon a good semiconductor?
Silicon atoms have four valence electrons. The valence electrons form a band that is filled, but the forbidden gap is so small that they can often reach the conduction band by means of their kinetic energy only. As a result, silicon conducts to a limited degree, so it's a good semiconductor.

3. Compare and contrast *n*-type semiconductors with *p*-type semiconductors.
Both are materials doped with sources of either electrons or holes to increase conductivity. An *n*-type semiconductor conducts by means of negatively charged electrons. A *p*-type semiconductor conducts by means of positively charged holes.

4. Why does a diode conduct charges in only one direction easily?
Free electrons on the *n*-end are attracted to the positively charged holes on the *p*-end of the diode. As a result of electron flow, the *n*-end is positive and the *p*-end is negative. The area around the junction is depleted of charge carriers and is a poor conductor. If the diode is connected to a circuit one way, the depletion layer increases and very little current flows. If the diode is connected the opposite way, the depletion layer is eliminated and current flows.

5. How does a supermarket bar-code scanner work?
It contains reverse-biased *pn*-junction diodes that detect laser light reflected from the bar codes. The light that falls on the junctions creates pairs of free electrons and holes. These are pulled toward the ends of the diodes, which results in a flow of current that depends on the light intensity.

Name ______

29 Chapter Assessment

6. Explain how an *npn* transistor works.
The *pn* junctions are like two back-to-back diodes. A battery keeps a positive potential difference between the collector and the emitter. The base-collector diode is reverse-biased, so no current flows, but a battery makes the base-emitter diode forward-biased. Conventional current flows from base to emitter, but most of the electrons pass through the base to the collector. The collector current causes a voltage drop across the resistor. Small changes in the voltage on the base amplify into large changes in the voltage drop across the resistor.

Answer the following questions, showing your calculations.

7. A forward-biased silicon diode is connected to a 6.0-V battery. Also in the circuit are three 220-Ω resistors connected in series. The voltage in the circuit is 0.7 V. What is the current?

$$V_b = IR + V_d$$
$$I = \frac{V_b - V_d}{R} = \frac{6.0\text{ V} - 0.7\text{ V}}{3(220\ \Omega)} = 8.0\text{ mA}$$

8. Intrinsic silicon has 1×10^{13} free electrons per centimeter. A doped silicon crystal has 4.99×10^{22} silicon atoms per cubic centimeter. The silicon is doped with arsenic so that one in every 1×10^{7} silicon atoms is replaced by an arsenic atom.

a. If each arsenic atom donates one electron to the conduction band, what is the density of free electrons in the resulting semiconductor?

$$\frac{\text{free e}^-}{\text{cm}^3} = \left(\frac{4.99 \times 10^{22}\text{ Si atoms}}{\text{cm}^3}\right)\left(\frac{1\text{ free e}^-}{\text{As atom}}\right)\left(\frac{1\text{ As atom}}{1 \times 10^{7}\text{ Si atoms}}\right) = 5 \times 10^{15}\text{ free e}^-/\text{cm}^3$$

b. By what ratio is the free-electron density in the doped silicon greater than that of intrinsic silicon?

$$\text{ratio} = \frac{\text{free e}^-/\text{cm}^3\text{ in doped Si}}{\text{free e}^-/\text{cm}^3\text{ in intrinsic Si}} = \frac{5 \times 10^{15}\text{ free e}^-/\text{cm}^3}{1 \times 10^{13}\text{ free e}^-/\text{cm}^3} = 500$$

c. Does conduction in the doped silicon take place mainly by means of thermally freed electrons of the silicon itself or by means of the arsenic-donated electrons? Give a reason for your answer.
Because there are about 500 arsenic-donated electrons for every electron donated by silicon, the conduction is mainly by the arsenic-donated electrons.

Date ______ Period ______ Name ______

30 Chapter Assessment

Use with Chapter 30.

The Nucleus

Understanding Concepts Part A

Write the letter of the choice that best completes the statement or answers the question.

b 1. An atom's atomic number refers to the ____.
a. number of neutrons in a atom
b. number of protons in a atom
c. half the atom's atomic mass
d. number of isotopes of the atom

d 2. The mass number of an atom is equal to ____.
a. the sum of its protons and electrons
b. twice its number of neutrons
c. half its atomic number
d. the sum of its protons and neutrons

c 3. All nuclides of an element have ____.
a. different numbers of protons
b. the same number of neutrons
c. the same number of protons
d. different numbers of electrons

b 4. The number of decays per second in a sample of radioactive material is its ____.
a. half-life
b. activity
c. gamma decay
d. nuclear reaction

b 5. Which type of radioactive decay occurs when a neutron changes to a proton within the nucleus?
a. alpha decay
b. beta decay
c. gamma decay
d. positron decay

a 6. The time required for half the atoms in a given quantity of a radioactive isotope to decay is the ____ of that element.
a. half-life
b. activity
c. ionization rate
d. weak interaction

c 7. Which of the following is a type of particle accelerator?
a. Geiger-Mueller tube
b. Wilson cloud chamber
c. synchrotron
d. vacuum container

d 8. Physicists believe that quarks make up ____.
a. neutrons and electrons
b. neutrinos and neutrons
c. protons and electrons
d. protons and neutrons

Name ______________________

30 Chapter Assessment

Understanding Concepts Part B

Answer the following questions.

1. The atomic mass of the most abundant isotope of bismuth is about 209 u. The atomic number of bismuth is 83. How many neutrons does an atom of this isotope of bismuth have?

   $n = A - p$

   $= 209 - 83$

   $= 126$

2. A radium atom, $^{224}_{88}Ra$, decays to radon, Rn, by emitting an α particle.

   a. Write a nuclear equation for this transmutation.

   $^{224}_{88}Ra \rightarrow ^{220}_{86}Rn + ^{4}_{2}He$

   b. What is the charge of the new nucleus?

   The charge of the new nucleus is +86.

3. An atom of plutonium, $^{243}_{94}Pu$, emits a β particle when its nucleus decays to americium, Am.

   a. Write a nuclear equation for this transmutation.

   $^{243}_{94}Pu \rightarrow ^{243}_{95}Am + ^{0}_{-1}e + ^{0}_{0}\bar{\nu}$

   b. Indicate the number of protons and neutrons in the americium nucleus.

   Am has 95 protons and 148 neutrons.

4. Complete the following equations.

   a. $^{253}_{99}Es + ^{4}_{2}He \rightarrow ^{256}_{101}Md +$ $^{1}_{0}n$

   b. $^{238}_{92}U + 17\ ^{1}_{0}n \rightarrow ^{255}_{100}Fm +$ $8\ ^{0}_{-1}e$

   c. $^{4}_{2}He + ^{9}_{4}Be \rightarrow$ $^{12}_{6}C$ $+ ^{1}_{0}n$

5. If a radioactive sample has an activity of 24 decays/s, what will the activity be after two half-lives have passed?

   $\text{activity} = (\text{activity}_i)(\tfrac{1}{2})^n$

   $= (24\ \text{decays/s})(\tfrac{1}{2})^2$

   $= 6\ \text{decays/s}$

Name ______________________

30 Chapter Assessment

Applying Concepts

Answer the following questions using complete sentences.

1. How can you calculate the mass of a nucleus?

   The mass of the nucleus is approximately equal to its mass number multiplied by the atomic mass unit (A × u).

2. Compare the penetrating abilities of alpha, beta, and gamma radiation. Give examples of shields capable of stopping the different types of radiation.

   Alpha radiation is the least penetrating; it can be stopped by a thick sheet of paper. Beta radiation is more penetrating; 6 mm of aluminum can stop most β particles. Gamma radiation is the most penetrating; several centimeters of lead can stop gamma rays.

3. Describe the effect gamma decay has on the mass number and atomic number of an atom.

   Since gamma radiation results from the redistribution of the charge within a nucleus, gamma decay does not change the mass number or the atomic number.

4. Compare the number of protons, neutrons, and electrons found in two neutral isotopes of the same element.

   Two isotopes of the same element have the same number of protons and electrons, but different numbers of neutrons.

Name ______________

30 Chapter Assessment

5. Since the total number of nuclear particles during a nuclear reaction stays the same, what must be true of an equation representing such a reaction?

The sum of the superscripts (mass numbers) on the right side of the equation must equal the sum of the superscripts on the left side of the equation.

6. Why can't a linear accelerator speed up neutrons?

Since a linear accelerator uses an electric field, it doesn't affect neutrons, which do not have an electrical charge.

7. Use the quark model to explain why a proton has a positive charge and a neutron has no charge.

The quark model describes a proton as a combination of three quarks, two up (charge of $\frac{2}{3}$e) and one down ($-\frac{1}{3}$e). The charge of the proton is the sum of the charges of the three quarks, which is +1. The quark model describes a neutron as a combination of one up quark and two down quarks. The sum of the charges of these three quarks is zero.

Name ______________

30 Chapter Assessment

Answer the following questions.

8. Geologists use the radioactive decay of $^{40}_{19}K$ to determine the ages of certain minerals. Assume that when the mineral is formed, $^{40}_{19}K$ is trapped in a crystal, but none of its decay products exist in the mineral at the time. The half-life of $^{40}_{19}K$ is 1.3×10^9 years. The decay products of $^{40}_{19}K$ are $^{40}_{18}Ar$ (12%) and $^{40}_{20}Ca$ (88%). An analysis of the mineral reveals that the ratio of $^{40}_{19}K$ to $^{40}_{18}Ar$ to $^{40}_{20}Ca$ is approximately 25:9:66.

a. What is the approximate age of the mineral? Give a reason for your answer.

The mineral is about 2.6×10^9 years old. After one half-life, the mass of the $^{40}_{19}K$ was one half of what it was when the mineral was formed. The decayed 50% consists of $^{40}_{18}Ar$ ($0.12 \times 50\%$, or 6%) and $^{40}_{20}Ca$ ($0.88 \times 50\%$, or 44%). After two half-lives, these figures would be 25% $^{40}_{19}K$, 9% $^{40}_{18}Ar$, and 66% $^{40}_{20}Ca$.

b. Write an equation for the transmutation of $^{40}_{19}K$ to $^{40}_{20}Ca$.

$$^{40}_{19}K \rightarrow {}^{40}_{20}Ca + {}^{0}_{-1}e + {}^{0}_{0}\bar{\nu}$$

c. Write an equation for the transmutation of $^{40}_{19}K$ to $^{40}_{18}Ar$.

$$^{40}_{19}K + {}^{0}_{-1}e \rightarrow {}^{40}_{18}Ar \quad or \quad {}^{40}_{19}K \rightarrow {}^{40}_{18}Ar + {}^{0}_{1}e + {}^{0}_{0}\nu$$

9. The half-life of $^{35}_{17}Cl$ is 2.5 s. It decays to sulfur, S, through emission of a positron.

a. If the mass of a sample of $^{35}_{17}Cl$ is 16 g, how much will remain after 15 s?

$$\text{half-lives} = \frac{15\text{ s}}{2.5\text{ s}} = 6$$

$$m = m_i\left(\tfrac{1}{2}\right)^n = (16\text{ g})\left(\tfrac{1}{2}\right)^6 = 0.25\text{ g}$$

b. Write a complete equation to represent the decay of $^{35}_{17}Cl$.

$$^{33}_{17}Cl \rightarrow {}^{33}_{16}S + {}^{0}_{1}e + {}^{0}_{0}\nu$$

Name ______________________

30 Chapter Assessment

10. The half-life of $^{52}_{25}$Mn is 5.6 days. What was the original mass of $^{52}_{25}$Mn if, after 50.4 days, 1.20 g are found?

$$\text{half-lives} = \frac{50.4 \text{ days}}{5.6 \text{ days}} = 9$$

$$m = m_i\left(\tfrac{1}{2}\right)^n$$

$$m_i = \frac{m}{\left(\tfrac{1}{2}\right)^n} = \frac{1.20 \text{ g}}{\left(\tfrac{1}{2}\right)^9} = 614 \text{ g}$$

11. In nature, $^{238}_{92}$U decay goes through 14 steps until a stable nuclide forms. The series below shows these 14 steps. Some information is missing at each step. Fill in the missing subscripts and superscripts for each nuclide. Label each arrow as alpha or beta decay.

$$^{238}_{92}\text{U} \xrightarrow{\alpha} {}^{234}_{90}\text{Th} \xrightarrow{\beta} {}^{234}_{91}\text{Pa} \xrightarrow{\beta} {}^{234}_{92}\text{U} \xrightarrow{\alpha} {}^{230}_{90}\text{Th} \xrightarrow{\alpha} {}^{226}_{88}\text{Ra} \xrightarrow{\alpha} {}^{222}_{86}\text{Rn} \xrightarrow{\alpha} {}^{218}_{84}\text{Po} \xrightarrow{\alpha}$$

$$^{214}_{82}\text{Pb} \xrightarrow{\beta} {}^{214}_{83}\text{Bi} \xrightarrow{\beta} {}^{214}_{84}\text{Po} \xrightarrow{\alpha} {}^{210}_{82}\text{Pb} \xrightarrow{\beta} {}^{210}_{83}\text{Bi} \xrightarrow{\beta} {}^{210}_{84}\text{Po} \xrightarrow{\alpha} {}^{206}_{82}\text{Pb}$$

Date ____________ Period ____________ Name ______________________

31 Chapter Assessment

Use with Chapter 31.

Nuclear Applications

Understanding Concepts Part A

For each of the statements below, write true or rewrite the italicized part to make the statement true.

1. **strong force** The range over which the *weak force* acts is about 1.3×10^{-15} m.
2. **true** Binding energy is the amount of energy required to separate the nucleus into individual *nucleons.*
3. **negative** The binding energy of the nucleus is *positive.*
4. **less** The mass of the assembled nucleus is *more* than the sum of the masses of the nucleons that compose it.
5. **true** In a nuclear reaction, the binding energy before the reaction is *less* than it is after the reaction.
6. **can** Radioactive isotopes *cannot* be formed artificially.

Write the letter of the choice that best completes each statement.

b **7.** The detection of _____ indicates the movement of isotopes through the body.
- **a.** charge
- **b.** decay products
- **c.** light
- **d.** changes in mass

c **8.** Nuclear fission refers to _____.
- **a.** a chemical reaction in which an atom dissociates into ions.
- **b.** the combining of two nuclei
- **c.** the division of a nucleus
- **d.** the separation of two atoms

a **9.** A moderator in a nuclear reactor decreases the speed of _____.
- **a.** neutrons
- **b.** electrons
- **c.** protons
- **d.** neutrinos

b **10.** The rate of a chain reaction is changed by _____.
- **a.** moderators
- **b.** control rods
- **c.** nucleons
- **d.** uranium rods

a **11.** In the fusion process in the sun, a helium nucleus forms from the _____.
- **a.** fusion of four hydrogen nuclei
- **b.** fusion of four neutrons
- **c.** transmutation of a hydrogen nucleus
- **d.** fission of a beryllium nucleus

Name ______

31 Chapter Assessment

Understanding Concepts Part B

Answer the following questions, showing your calculations.

1. The nuclear mass of $^{101}_{44}Ru$ is 100.9 u.
   a. What is the ruthenium's mass defect?
   total mass = 44(1.007825 u) + 57(1.008665 u)
   = 101.83821 u
   mass defect = $m_T - m_{Ru}$
   = 101.8321 u − 100.9 u
   = 0.9 u
   b. What is the ruthenium's binding energy in MeV?
   energy = (0.9 u)(931.49 MeV/u)
   = 8×10^2 MeV
2. Write the nuclear equation for beta decay: $^{94}_{43}Tc$ to ruthenium, Ru
   $^{94}_{43}Tc \rightarrow ^{94}_{44}Ru + ^{0}_{-1}e + ^{0}_{0}\bar{\nu}$
3. Write the nuclear equation for alpha decay: $^{144}_{60}Nd$ to cesium, Ce
   $^{144}_{60}Nd \rightarrow ^{140}_{58}Ce + ^{4}_{2}He$
4. Write an equation for the following change: $^{174}_{73}Ta$ emits a positron, and forms hafnium, Hf.
   $^{174}_{73}Ta \rightarrow ^{174}_{72}Hf + ^{0}_{1}e + ^{0}_{0}\nu$
5. The human thyroid gland uses iodine to produce vital hormones. Based on this fact, scientists have devised ways of using radioactive $^{131}_{53}I$ to measure the functions of the thyroid.
   a. $^{131}_{53}I$ decays to xenon, Xe, by emission of a β particle. What isotope of xenon is formed?
   The isotope is $^{131}_{54}Xe$.
   b. Write the equation for this reaction.
   $^{131}_{53}I \rightarrow ^{131}_{54}Xe + ^{0}_{-1}e$
   c. The half-life of $^{131}_{53}I$ is approximately eight days. If a patient is given a 6.0-mg dose of $^{131}_{53}I$ on a Monday, how much $^{131}_{53}I$ will remain in the patient's body eight days later?
   $M = m_i (\frac{1}{2})^n$
   $= (6.0 \text{ mg})(\frac{1}{2})^1$
   $= 3.0$ mg

Name ______

31 Chapter Assessment

Applying Concepts

Answer the following questions, using complete sentences.

1. Explain how the mass defect relates to the equation $E = mc^2$.
   The energy equivalent of the mass defect can be calculated with $E = mc^2$.
2. Under what circumstances is energy released by a nuclear reaction?
   Energy will be released if the nucleus that is a product of the reaction is more tightly bound than the original nucleus.
3. How did Lise Meitner and Otto Frisch explain the production of small atoms, such as barium, from uranium atoms?
   Uranium nuclei were split by neutrons to form new products, including barium nuclei.
4. What is the function of a moderator in a nuclear reactor?
   Moderators collide with fast neutrons, slowing their motion. Having more slow neutrons increases the probability of the fission of $^{235}_{92}U$ nuclei in the reactor, which produce more neutrons that can split other $^{235}_{92}U$ nuclei. Thus, moderators help keep chain reactions going.
5. What is the Cerenkov effect and what causes it?
   The Cerenkov effect is a blue glow when nuclear fuel rods hit water. High-energy electrons enter the water at speeds exceeding the speed of light in water to produce the glow.
6. Compare the amount of energy released when a dynamite molecule reacts chemically to the amount of energy released by the fusion of a helium nucleus.
   The energy released from one dynamite molecule during a chemical reaction is about 20 eV while that released by the fusion of one helium molecule is 25 MeV. The fusion reaction releases 1.25 million times more energy than the chemical reaction.

Name ______________

31 Chapter Assessment

7. Describe how a magnetic field is used to control fusion.

Magnetic fields can confine charged particles; the reactants for a fusion are at such a high temperature that they cannot be held in containers made of any known material. When the intensity of the magnetic field is suddenly increased, the pressure produced increases the temperature of the contained plasma to a point where fusion can take place.

Answer the following questions, showing your calculations.

8. A sample of a pure isotope of berkelium, Bk, decays to produce an isotope of curium, $^{248}_{96}Cm$. In this process, the nucleus captures an orbiting electron.

a. Write an equation for this decay.

$$^{248}_{97}Bk + {}^{0}_{-1}e \rightarrow {}^{248}_{96}Cm$$

b. What was the original isotope of berkelium?

The original isotope was $^{248}_{97}Bk$.

9. The energy released in the fission of one atom of $^{239}_{94}Pu$ is 1.6 MeV.

a. How many atoms are in 2.0 kg of pure $^{239}_{94}Pu$?

$$n = \frac{(6.02 \times 10^{23}\ \text{atoms/mole})(2.0\ \text{kg})}{0.239\ \text{kg/mole}}$$

$$= 5.0 \times 10^{24}\ \text{atoms}$$

b. How much energy would be released if all these atoms underwent fission?

$$E = (5.0 \times 10^{24}\ \text{atoms})(1.6\ \text{MeV/atom})$$

$$= 8.0 \times 10^{24}\ \text{MeV}$$

10. An $^{252}_{99}Es$ nucleus (mass = 252.0829 u) decays to $^{248}_{97}Bk$ (mass = 248.0702 u) by emitting an α particle (mass = 4.0026 u) with a kinetic energy of 6.64 MeV. What is the kinetic energy of the berkelium nucleus?

$$\text{mass defect} = (252.0829\ \text{u}) - (248.0702\ \text{u} + 4.0026\ \text{u})$$

$$= 0.0101\ \text{u}$$

$$KE = (0.0101\ \text{u})(931.49\ \text{MeV/u})$$

$$= 9.41\ \text{MeV}$$

$$KE_{Bk} = KE_T - KE_{He}$$

$$= (9.41\ \text{MeV}) - (6.64\ \text{MeV})$$

$$= 2.77\ \text{MeV}$$

11. If 1.806×10^{24} atoms of $^{235}_{92}U$ undergo fission and produce 1.0×10^{13} J, how much energy is produced per kilogram of $^{235}_{92}U$?

$$E = \left(\frac{1.0 \times 10^{13}\ \text{J}}{1.806 \times 10^{24}\ \text{atoms}}\right)\left(\frac{6.02 \times 10^{23}\ \text{atoms}}{1\ \text{mole}}\right)\left(\frac{1\ \text{mole}}{0.235\ \text{kg}}\right)$$

$$= 1.4 \times 10^{13}\ \text{J}$$